Hypnotic Techniques for Chronic Pain Management:

Favorite Methods of Master Clinicians

Edited by Mark P. Jensen, PhD

Denny Creek Press

Denny
Creek
Press

Cover art by Liza Brown of Modern Art Media
Interior design by Elizabeth Beeton of B10 Mediaworx

Library of Congress Cataloging-in-Publication Data
        Hypnotic Techniques for Chronic Pain Management: Favorite Methods of Master Clinicians / Mark P. Jensen, editor.
                                        p. cm.
        Includes bibliographic references
        ISBN 978-1-946832-08-5 (alk. paper)
        1. Hypnotism—Therapeutic Use   2. Psychotherapy

*This book is dedicated to
David R. Patterson and Joseph Barber,
to whom I will be forever indebted for introducing
me to the fascinating world of hypnosis*

About the *Voices of Experience*™ series

Research demonstrates that experienced hypnosis practitioners obtain better outcomes than hypnosis practitioners who are relatively new to the field. For example, Barabasz and colleagues found that the participants in a study of smoking cessation who were treated by clinicians experienced in the use of hypnosis evidenced over *four times* greater treatment response than participants who were treated by clinical psychology interns with minimal training (Barabasz et al., 1986). Although this finding may seem intuitively obvious, clinician experience has *not* been found to play a role in outcome for many other (nonhypnotic) psychological therapies (Berman & Norton, 1985; Durlak, 1979; Shapiro & Shapiro, 1982).

Thus, hypnosis outcomes appear to be particularly sensitive to the benefits of experience. This makes sense, given that hypnosis involves the creative application of specific techniques for enhancing patient readiness to accept new ideas (i.e., the hypnotic induction; Jensen, 2017), as well as the skilled use of language to develop and offer suggestions for changes in how the patient feels, thinks, or behaves. By observing the patient's immediate and longer-term response to treatment, clinicians discover and refine effective techniques and hone their use of language. Through this process, they learn what works and what does not work.

Given the widespread use of hypnosis, clinicians in some regions will likely discover and develop techniques that other clinicians may not have (yet) discovered. Thus, there are master clinicians worldwide who are using effective methods that clinicians in other parts of the world may not have heard of or discovered yet.

Unfortunately, while many of the world's most experienced clinicians facilitate workshops in their own countries in which they pass on their wisdom, they do not necessarily teach at international conferences such as the tri-annual World Congress of Medical and Clinical Hypnosis (www.ishhypnosis.org). Nor is every practicing clinician able to participate in workshops that are offered around world. The purpose of the *Voices of Experience*™ series is to give practicing clinicians access to the wealth of knowledge held by master clinicians throughout the world, in order to increase the ease and efficacy of treatment.

To make this information easily accessible, in the chapters contained in the series' books, the authors describe the theory or ideas that underlie their favorite hypnotic approaches and techniques. They also provide a specific transcript or scripts that illustrate the techniques or approaches they find useful, along with commentary. Thus, each chapter is much like having an opportunity to participate in workshops offered by the authors. I hope and anticipate that readers will enjoy learning, and then incorporating into their practice, the wisdom and experience shared in this series.

Mark P. Jensen
Editor, *Voices of Experience*™

References

Barabasz, A. F., Baer, L., Sheehan, D. V., & Barabasz, M. (1986). A three-year follow-up of hypnosis and restricted environmental stimulation therapy for smoking. *International Journal of Clinical and Experimental Hypnosis, 34*, 169-181.

Berman, J. S., & Norton, N. C. (1985). Does professional training make a therapist more effective? *Psychological Bulletin, 98,* 401-407.

Durlak, J. A. (1979). Comparative effectiveness of paraprofessional and professional helpers. *Psychological Bulletin, 86,* 80-92.

Jensen, M. P. (2017). *The art and practice of hypnotic induction: Favorite methods of master clinicains.* Kirkland, WA: Denny Creek Press.

Shapiro, D. A., & Shapiro, D. (1982). Meta-analysis of comparative therapy outcome studies: a replication and refinement. *Psychological Bulletin, 92,* 581-604.

CONTRIBUTORS

Giuseppe De Benedittis, MD, PhD
University of Milano
Milano, Italy
giuseppe.debenedittis@unimi.it

Hansjörg Ebell, Dr. med
Private Practice
Munich, Germany
www.doktorebell.de

Roxanna Erickson-Klein, RN, LPC, PhD
Private Practice
Dallas, TX, USA
REricksonKlein@Gmail.com
Erickson-Klein.org

Mark P. Jensen, PhD, FASCH
University of Washington
Seattle, WA, USA
mjensen@uw.edu

Daniel P. Kohen, MD, FAAP, ABMH
National Pediatric Hypnosis Training
    Institute (NPHTI)
University of Minnesota
Minneapolis, MN, USA
dpkohen@umn.edu

Leora Kuttner, PhD
University of British Columbia and BC
    Children's Hospital
Vancouver, BC, Canada
kuttner@sfu.ca

Shigeru Matsuki, LCP, Chmn JSCH,
    FJSH
Private Practice
Kyoto, Japan
k6950605@kadai.jp

Miyuki Mizutani, PhD
Aichi Medical University
Nagakute, Aichi, Japan
st-neige@i-live.ne.jp

Stella C. Nkenke, Dr. med
Private Practice
Buckenhof, Germany
Vienna, Austria
praxis@nkenke.de

Olafur S. Palsson, PsyD
Department of Medicine
University of North Carolina at Chapel
    Hill
Chapel Hill, NC, USA
opalsson@med.unc.edu

David R. Patterson, PhD
University of Washington
Seattle, WA, USA
davepatt@uw.edu

Burkhard Peter, Dipl Psych
Ludwig-Maximilians Universität
    München and MEG-Stiftung
    and Private Practice
Munich, Germany
burkhard-peter@t-online.de

Alan O. Szmelskyj, DO, MSc, Adv Dip
    Clin Hyp, FRSPH
Private Practice
True Health Clinics
Godmanchester, UK
alan@truehealthclinics.com

CONTENTS

CHAPTER 1

Introduction

Mark P. Jensen

Chronic pain, usually defined as pain that persists for three months or more following initial onset, is a common and costly problem worldwide. As many as 37% of individuals in developed countries and 41% of individuals in developing countries report having had chronic pain in the previous 12 months (Tsang et al., 2008). Chronic pain is also a common comorbid problem associated with many health conditions, such as cancer, diabetes, multiple sclerosis, and spinal cord injury.

Chronic pain can, and for many people does, contribute to depression, sleep problems, relationship difficulties, vocational dysfunction, and inactivity. Through various biological and behavioral mechanisms, these negative effects of pain can themselves then result in more pain. This can create a "vicious cycle" of pain leading to depression, sleep problems, and disability, then increased pain, with subsequent worsening depression, sleep problems and disability (Bunzli et al., 2017; Tanik et al., 2016). In this way, and over time, pain and its associated negative effects can become self-perpetuating, long after the original injury associated with pain onset has healed.

By the time the pain problem is diagnosed as a chronic condition, many patients have received numerous biomedical treatments, including analgesic medications, surgeries, and medical procedures (e.g., "nerve blocks"). However, these biomedical treatments often target mechanisms that are no longer causing or maintaining the pain problem. Hence, while they might produce some temporary relief for some patients, biomedical interventions rarely have sustained benefits (Novy et al., 1995). Moreover, many of the biomedical treatments that are commonly provided to relieve chronic pain can cause adverse events and physical changes that contribute to more pain over time, making the problem worse rather than better (Annemans, 2011; Davis et al., 2017; Machado et al., 2017).

Over the past two decades, a growing body of research has demonstrated the beneficial effects of hypnosis and training in self-hypnosis for reducing pain and pain-related disability in individuals with chronic pain (Adachi et al., 2014; Jensen, 2009; Patterson & Jensen, 2003). The reason hypnosis is helpful for so many people is that it does, in fact, effectively target the central nervous system mechanisms that are maintaining the pain (Jensen et al., 2015). The purpose of this book is to provide clinicians working with patients who have been given the diagnosis of chronic pain specific examples of hypnotic techniques and approaches that master clinicians have found in their extensive clinical experience to be most effective.

In the first of these chapters (Chapter 2 of this book), David R. Patterson emphasizes the multifactorial biopsychosocial nature of pain. He makes the important point that patients who carry a diagnosis of chronic pain should be assessed from a biopsychosocial perspective, in order to identify the most important treatment goals. He notes that for some patients the most important treatment goal might not be pain reduction. He then describes a treatment approach based on both biopsychosocial and Ericksonian perspectives, incorporating many classic Ericksonian strategies. This includes use of a nonlinear induction, and suggestions that make use of confusion, truisms, indirect suggestions, metaphors, and patient choice. The specific example he provides illustrates this approach beautifully.

In Chapter 3, Alan O. Szmelskyj also notes the complexity of chronic pain—in this case, chronic back pain—and the importance of a thorough assessment that identifies the factors that are contributing to the patient's pain. He points out that among the most common contributors to the perpetuation of pain are negative beliefs about the pain, low levels of activity, fear of pain, depression, and a history of traumatic life events. For back pain especially, fear of movement and inactivity are often key. To address these issues, he provides an example of an induction and suggestions that use imagery, age regression and age progression to increase comfort associated with increases in activity and movement.

In the Chapter 4, Giuseppe De Benedittis provides a thorough state-of-the-science review of the pathogenesis of fibromyalgia syndrome (FMS). He notes that while there is not yet consensus among experts regarding the best treatments for FMS, multimodal and multidisciplinary treatments—especially those that include cognitive behavioral therapy—are commonly recommended. At the same time, there is a growing body of research supporting hypnosis as a promising treatment for FMS. Professor De Benedittis provides two examples of scripts that he has found to be effective in his clinical work. One example includes an induction followed by suggestions that utilize imagery for achieving comfort, well-being, energy, and a positive body image. The second uses age regression to recover and nurture inner resources and suggestions to instill expectations for a positive future life.

Chronic pain is also a common comorbidity of gastrointestinal (GI) conditions. In chapter 5, Olafur S. Palsson cites the extensive evidence supporting the efficacy of hypnosis in the treatment of GI pain. He presents a model of hypnotic treatment that includes: (1) maximizing the patient's receptive state, (2) presenting suggestions that target the four components of GI-related pain, and (3) linking the suggestions for improvements to imagery. The script he presents clearly demonstrates these principals.

In chapter 6, Stella C. Nkenke describes how hypnosis can benefit patients with complex regional pain syndrome (CRPS). Having had a history of CRPS herself gives her a unique perspective on this complex and challenging condition. Because treating CRPS soon after it develops can make recovery easier, it is extremely important for clinicians to recognize this condition. Hence, Dr. Nkenke's description of the clinical presentation and diagnostic criteria for CRPS is a critical component of the chapter. Treatment of CRPS is complicated, and no single treatment has been found to be universally effective. Dr. Nkenke points out that successful outcomes with CRPS treatment require that the patient do regular home practice of the skills they have been taught. The example treatment that Dr. Nkenke describes includes suggestions for an integration of the affected body part (with CRPS, this is most often the arm or leg) and nurturing associations between the CRPS diagnostic label and positive emotions and goals.

In Chapter 7, I discuss three facts about chronic pain that have important implications for the clinical use of hypnosis in providing comfort to patients: (1) pain is the end result of a complex interaction of activity in different parts of the brain and body; (2) pain is an experience *created* by the brain, not a "sensation" perceived by the brain; and (3) there are five clear strategies that clinicians can incorporate into their hypnosis sessions that will enhance outcomes. After reviewing these, I describe and provide examples of six evidence-based approaches, each designed to help patients who have chronic pain experience greater comfort.

In chapter 8, Shigeru Matsuki emphasizes the critical importance of tailoring treatment to each patient's goals and needs. He presents the case of a patient with chronic pain who did not respond to a number of standardized hypnotic treatments (i.e., hypnotic approaches with demonstrated efficacy, "on average"), and who required a unique approach to address his chronic pain problem. In this case study, Professor Matsuki also shows how it is possible to listen carefully for the meaning underlying the many verbal and non-verbal communications provided by patients, and to incorporate this understanding into treatment. His case study illustrates the point that, given their experience with refractory cases, master clinicians are in an excellent position to discover and contribute new treatments that optimize efficacy. These treatments then have the potential to prompt further research into the factors contributing to therapeutic success.

In Chapter 9, Burkhard Peter describes two hypnotic techniques that he has found especially useful for helping patients with chronic pain. The first involves helping patients create an internal representation of pain that they can then change from a physical/kinesthetic experience to an alternative (visual, auditory, or tactile) sensory experience. He has found this technique to be particularly effective when the pain problem is focal and when the pain is not playing an important functional (e.g., social) role for the patient. The second technique is more effective for patients with more diffuse pain and/or with those for whom psychosocial factors may be playing a larger role. It involves inviting the patient to create in his or her imagination both a "symptom carrier" and an "anti-symptom carrier" who, respectively, do and do not have the same symptoms as the patient. Imagined interactions between the patient and these two "individuals" then allows the patient to gain important insight into his or her own pain problem.

Milton H. Erickson is well known for his use of hypnosis to assist individuals presenting with many problems and conditions, including chronic pain. In Chapter 10, Roxanna Erickson-Klein describes the various strategies that Milton Erickson used for treating chronic pain, and then provides detailed scripts and descriptions from his writings as examples of these strategies. She complements this information with a case study of a patient with a history of a back injury, treated in an integrated way using the Ericksonian techniques and approaches she describes.

In Chapter 11, Miyuki Mizutani summarizes the hypnotic approach she has developed for use in the context of a multidisciplinary pain treatment program. She has found it useful to think of hypnosis treatment as involving two distinct phases. The initial phase lasts until the patient first experiences a clinically meaningful—but not necessarily (yet) durable—decrease in pain during a session. During the second phase, the patient learns to use hypnosis to maintain the comfort achieved and can then experience this comfort outside of the session and in his or her daily life. Dr. Mizutani notes the importance of avoiding negative ideas and suggestions during treatment (i.e., to avoid referring to the patient's pain as "chronic," which implies that it will not change). She presents two transcripts of sessions that illustrate her approach, including a number of suggestions for helping patients to experience changes in their pain.

In Chapter 12, Hansjörg Ebell emphasizes the importance of the patient-clinician relationship in developing a treatment plan. The patient has expertise with respect to his or her experience and available resources, and the clinician has expert knowledge about the biological, psychological, and social factors that can contribute to pain and dysfunction, as well as the treatments that can influence these. Together, the patient and clinician can use their respective areas of expertise to help the patient change focus. Central to this change is the identification of the appropriate (hypnotic) suggestions that will help a patient make a shift from viewing pain as something to be fought against or removed (i.e., the biomedical "find and fix it" approach to pain management), towards a focus on nurturing the patient's resources and identifying solutions for achieving well-being. Dr. Ebell presents a case study that illustrates how this process can be successfully applied in a patient with complex regional pain syndrome.

Leora Kuttner notes in Chapter 13 that patients often receive messages from health care providers that can be both inaccurate and disheartening. Being told that, "There is nothing we can do about your pain" can leave patients feeling helpless. Thus, a critical component of pain treatment is to provide patients with accurate, state-of-the-science information about pain. A key message is that the patient's pain is only "chronic until it changes, then it's not." She describes and then provides an example of a specific favorite hypnotic technique—the Pain Switch—that on the surface targets pain reduction but also facilitates the development of self-efficacy and self-management skills.

Finally, in Chapter 14, Daniel P. Kohen emphasizes the importance of rapport in effective use of hypnosis and how clinicians can facilitate this. In his work, he is extremely attentive to his and the patient's language, and he gently interrupts any "negative" words. The example transcript he offers of a session with a 12-year-old boy presenting with frequent migraine headaches shows how he uses hypnotic language to develop rapport, re-frame the presenting symptoms, identify patient resources, and increase outcome expectations and motivation. He then demonstrates how he integrates this all into a formal hypnotic experience.

Universal Issues

There are some consistent threads that run through all or nearly all of the chapters. These threads of consistency likely represent "universal" ideas that may be particularly important in the hypnotic treatment of chronic pain in all contexts. They include the ideas that: (1) pain is a complex biopsychosocial phenomenon; (2) because each patient is unique, with different biological, psychological, and social factors contributing to his or her pain problem, treatment must be tailored to each particular patient; (3) because pain impacts many quality of life domains, and these domains can then impact pain, treatment often needs to target other outcomes in addition to (and sometimes instead of) pain intensity; and (4) a key underlying principal in chronic pain treatment is patient empowerment.

Pain is a Complex Biopsychosocial Phenomenon

Virtually every author discussed the fact that pain is complex, and most noted that biological, psychological, and social factors contribute to the severity of pain and its impact on a patient's life. This point was central to Patterson's chapter (as indicated by the use of the term "biopsychosocial" in his chapter title, see Chapter 2), but was also mentioned by the majority of the master clinicians who wrote chapters for this book. These discussions emphasize a critical point made by Melzack and Wall over 50 years ago: pain is not only the result of the amount of damage done to tissue (Melzack & Wall, 1965).

In fact, for many individuals who might carry the diagnosis of chronic pain, the amount of tissue damage present plays little to no role in the amount of pain the brain creates. Instead, pain is created by the brain automatically (i.e., without conscious control or influence) in order to protect the individual from potential harm in response to multiple physiological, psychological, and social cues (cf. Moseley & Butler, 2015). It is likely that the automatic and non-conscious nature of pain's creation is one of the reasons that hypnosis and hypnotic treatments are so effective for chronic pain management, given hypnosis' ability to impact these processes.

Hypnotic Treatment Should be Tailored to Each Patient

Given the complexity of pain and the many factors that contribute to and influence its creation, it is extremely unlikely that the same factors are contributing to the pain of any two or more patients. Two patients may report an average pain intensity level of "7" on a 0-10 scale, but the biological, psychological, and social factors that contribute to this level "7" are almost always, if not always, different for each patient. This means that it is imperative for clinicians to perform a thorough biological, psychological, and social assessment of each patient. If the clinician does not have expertise in any one of these domains, then it is ethically important to ensure that the patient *has* received a thorough evaluation by the appropriate experts. For example, psychologists should not begin treating patients with a history of chronic pain until they know that the patient has had a thorough medical evaluation by an appropriately trained health care professional, and the psychologist has access to the results of that evaluation. Once an understanding has been reached of the patient's circumstances in each of the three domains, treatment goals and approaches should be developed with this understanding in mind.

Moreover, even when one domain (e.g., psychological) plays a more important role to a particular patient's pain problem than other domains (e.g., biological or social), within that domain, the contributing factors are going to differ from one patient to another. For example, within the psychological domain, for some a critical issue might be fear of movement. For others, it might be a focus on the search for a biomedical "cure" and a lack of self-efficacy regarding pain management. For still others, the most important issue might be a preponderance of negative ("catastrophizing") self-talk that inhibits positive change.

Thus, it is important for clinicians to (1) be aware of the different factors within a particular domain that could potentially be contributing to the patient's pain experience, (2) identify the factors that are playing the most important roles in any particular patient's problem, and (3) develop a treatment plan that addresses each factor, as appropriate. The good news is that hypnosis can be used to facilitate the treatment of many of these factors, as illustrated in the chapters presented in this book.

Hypnosis Can (and Should) be Used to Facilitate Change in a Variety of Pain Outcomes

Although many patients with pain seek treatment with an initial primary goal of experiencing a reduction in the intensity of their usual pain, many of the authors in this volume noted that pain intensity need not be the only—or necessarily the primary—treatment target. Individuals with a history of ongoing pain can, and often do, report disruption in their sleep, mood, relationships, ability to work outside the home, and ability to engage in physical activities. As discussed previously, disruption in any of these areas can contribute to increased pain.

Thus, and paradoxically for many patients, if treatment focuses *only* on pain reduction without also targeting improvements in sleep quality, mood, and tolerance for activity, overall improvements in pain intensity may be limited. Readers may consider paying particular attention to the chapters that include discussion and hypnotic approaches which offer suggestions for improving these other critical outcomes. For example:

- "You see yourself moving fluidly, comfortably... just loving life. And that feeling fills your entire body. ... And maybe you will be curious about how you fall into a deep, profound, restful sleep when your head hits the pillow..." (Patterson, Chapter 2).

- "You may want to allow yourself now, and in the future, to walk just a little bit more, a little bit more than you used to…" (Szmelskyj, Chapter 3).

- "You are becoming happy, confident, energetic, and are progressing toward making yourself the best you that you can be… [an] incredible experience of well-being, full of energy…" (De Benedittis, Chapter 4).

- "…perhaps you are stronger… perhaps more fit… you have made important steps towards goals that are most meaningful to you… and succeeded. You can see how wonderful you feel. … Seeing your future self very vividly now… perhaps there is a smile on your face… the way you move…" (Jensen, Chapter 6).

- "Respect the need to balance rest with the productivity of work…" (Erickson-Klein, Chapter 10).

Treatment Should Include
a Focus on Patient Empowerment

Almost all of the authors discuss how the techniques they use are helpful for increasing patient self-efficacy for managing pain. Even as they emphasize the importance of automaticity of the treatment benefits—that benefits can and often do occur without any perceived effort on the part of the patient—these master clinicians teach patients how to use self-hypnosis to help maintain and expand these benefits.

These clinicians emphasize self-efficacy, self-control, and patient confidence in large part because they recognize that ongoing pain can undermine a patient's sense of self-efficacy and control over their lives, and control over the activities that they find most meaningful and valuable. Thus, careful readers will recognize both the implicit and explicit focus on patient empowerment and self-efficacy in the hypnotic scripts offered. For example:

- "… allow yourself to see your body and your back move gently side to side; all the while, feeling in control… the great pleasure and fun you feel as under your own control. … And enjoy how much better and more confident and comfortable you've become at doing what you want to do, and need to do…" (Szmelskyj, Chapter 3).

- "…continuing to move onward… you are in full control…" (De Benedittis, Chapter 4).

- "Would you be willing to learn a technique that draws on what you've learned today… one that empowers you to be the boss of your own body? … and gives you back some control over your sensations, so that you can start feeling better?" (Kuttner, Chapter 13).

Research evidence and clinical experience demonstrate that hypnosis and hypnotic strategies are effective for helping individuals who have been given a diagnosis of chronic pain. The authors who have contributed chapters to this volume represent the most experienced and knowledgeable clinicians working in this field throughout the world today. By learning and then using the strategies and techniques described here, clinicians will acquire additional tools to effectively help their patients improve comfort and achieve their most valued goals.

References

Adachi, T., Fujino, H., Nakae, A., Mashimo, T., & Sasaki, J. (2014). A meta-analysis of hypnosis for chronic pain problems: A comparison between hypnosis, standard care, and other psychological interventions. *International Journal of Clinical and Experimental Hypnosis, 62,* 1-28.

Annemans, L. (2011). Pharmacoeconomic impact of adverse events of long-term opioid treatment for the management of persistent pain. *Clinical Drug Investigation, 31,* 73-86.

Bunzli, S., Smith, A., Schutze, R., Lin, I., & O'Sullivan, P. (2017). Making sense of low back pain and pain-related fear. *Journal of Orthopaedic & Sports Physical Therapy, 47,* 628-636.

Davis, M. P., Behm, B., & Balachandran, D. (2017). Looking both ways before crossing the street: Assessing the benefits and risk of opioids in treating patients at risk of sleep-disordered breathing for pain and dyspnea. *Journal of Opioid Management, 13,* 183-196.

Jensen, M. P. (2009). Hypnosis for chronic pain management: A new hope. *Pain, 146,* 235-237.

Jensen, M. P., Adachi, T., Tomé-Pires, C., Lee, J., Osman, Z. J., & Miró, J. (2015). Mechanisms of hypnosis: Towards the development of a biopsychosocial model. *International Journal of Clinical and Experimental Hypnosis, 63,* 34-75.

Machado, G. C., Maher, C. G., Ferreira, P. H., Harris, I. A., Deyo, R. A., McKay, D., ... Ferreira, M. L. (2017). Trends, complications, and costs for hospital admission and surgery for lumbar spinal stenosis. *Spine, 42,* 1737-1743.

Melzack, R., & Wall, P. D. (1965). Pain mechanisms: A new theory. *Science, 150,* 971-979.

Moseley, G. L., & Butler, D. S. (2015). Fifteen years of explaining pain: The past, present, and future. *Journal of Pain, 16,* 807-813.

Novy, D. M., Nelson, D. V., Francis, D. J., & Turk, D. C. (1995). Perspectives of chronic pain: An evaluative comparison of restrictive and comprehensive models. *Psychological Bulletin, 118,* 238-247.

Patterson, D. R., & Jensen, M. P. (2003). Hypnosis and clinical pain. *Psychological Bulletin, 129,* 495-521.

Tanik, N., Sarp, U., Ucar, M., Celikbilek, A., Balbaloglu, O., Ak, H., ... Inan, L. E. (2016). Pain, depression and sleep disorders in patients with diabetic and nondiabetic carpal tunnel syndrome: A vicious cycle. *Arquivos de Neuro-Psiquiatria, 74,* 207-211.

Tsang, A., Von Korff, M., Lee, S., Alonso, J., Karam, E., Angermeyer, M. C., ... Watanabe, M. (2008). Common chronic pain conditions in developed and developing countries: Gender and age differences and comorbidity with depression-anxiety disorders. *Journal of Pain, 9,* 883-891.

CHAPTER 2

A Multilayered, Biopsychosocial Approach to Chronic Pain

David R. Patterson

David R. Patterson is a Professor of Psychology in the Departments of Rehabilitation Medicine, Surgery, and Psychology at the University of Washington School of Medicine, located in Seattle, Washington, USA. He is internationally recognized for his work in the area of hypnosis for pain control, as well as the psychology of burn and trauma injuries. Dr. Patterson is the author of Clinical Hypnosis for Pain Control, *published by APA in 2010 (Patterson, 2010), as well as over 150 articles and book chapters. He has been funded by the National Institutes of Health for his work using hypnosis and virtual reality since 1989, and one of his grants with this agency continues to this date. He has received numerous awards for his work in hypnosis.*

* * *

Chronic pain is an inordinately complex issue to treat by any means. In a sense, we are often chasing a phantom when attempting to manage chronic pain. As Bill Fordyce taught us decades ago, when treating chronic pain, we are really addressing suffering rather than pain (Fordyce, 1976).

What patients view as pain is often a neurophysiological remnant of stimulus-response conditioning that persists long after the original etiology for the pain has resolved. What patients view as chronic pain may be a manifestation of depression, a tendency to amplify physiological symptoms, or conditioned responses to family or work dynamics. Then again, there are many instances when a damaged nervous system is sending signals to the brain that defy imagination with respect to the misery they create.

For many patients, if not most, chronic pain is a multifaceted clinical issue, the management of which is based on a foundation of careful assessment. Moreover, effective treatment is based on something other than merely pain relief and should almost always (if not always) include: (1) increasing activity, (2) setting appropriate life goals, (3) addressing depression, and (4) altering contingencies that maintain pain behaviors. Often these methods may also surpass analgesia as a primary treatment goal. Yet the clinician is faced with the conundrum of which facet(s) of pain (and its impact) to address with what type(s) of suggestion(s). This chapter will present the use of a biopsychosocial assessment to determine the critical facets of pain-related suffering using a paradigm for hypnosis that is broad enough to encompass multiple treatment goals. The induction is based on work in this area I published in *Clinical Hypnosis for Pain Control* (Patterson, 2010). Before addressing this model, it will be important to discuss a hypnotic approach design that may be used specifically for pain reduction.

A Biopsychosocial, Multilayered Approach

The biopsychosocial approach to be discussed here differs from other approaches to chronic pain management that teach patients directly to reduce pain sensations through repetition and discipline. Some excellent examples of directly managing the experience of chronic pain can be found in many of the chapters in this volume. Moreover, focusing directly on pain reduction may be appropriate for some patients presenting with chronic pain at some point during treatment.

However, the approach that is most effective will depend on the clinical presentation of the patient. The approach proposed here focuses on lifestyle and other elements of suffering as much as, or more than, on pain itself. Further, it uses a nonlinear approach that is deliberately unpredictable. The approach attempts to create a state of mind that is highly receptive to hypnotic suggestion based on elements of confusion and metaphor that are designed to interfere with logical processing. Thus, rather than a disciplined approach that fosters repetition and learning, this model seeks to create an experience that patients can listen to repeatedly and will find unpredictable in its impact; specifically, that each time patients hear the induction they will "hear" it a different way, and therefore they may be able to approach their pain at a different level.

This clinical treatment model is based on a biopsychosocial assessment approach combined with an Ericksonian approach to hypnosis. The multilayered facet of the intervention is based on the use of biopsychosocial assessment to define elements of the patient's chronic pain that are based on any number of relevant domains (e.g., quality of the pain, coping style, cognitive function, psychodynamics, motivators for change, fear of change, illusionary attachments).

The Ericksonian approach to the induction allows the patient to entertain multiple levels of suggestion, to choose a preferable one in the moment, and to hold opposing concepts simultaneously. It also provides a framework to present suggestions in a nonlinear progression. Thus, this hypnotic approach is ideal for addressing a clinical problem as typically complex as chronic pain.

Biopsychosocial Assessment

Although the biopsychosocial approach to assessment in chronic illness is now the standard in the field (Patterson, 2010), it is seldom presented or discussed in the hypnosis literature. The biopsychosocial approach assesses biological, psychological, and social perspectives. With respect to chronic pain assessment, the biological component refers to physiological factors that can be addressed through traditional medicine. Thus, the biological part of assessment would include variables such as the intensity, quality, and location of the pain. Such information might lead to different medication choices (e.g., neuropathic pain is addressed with different medications than musculoskeletal pain), types of procedures (e.g., high-intensity acute pain may suggest epidural anesthesia), or surgical intervention (obviously determined by the location of the pain as well as by several other factors). No competent clinician can proceed with a pain assessment without an understanding of the biological factors contributing to the pain problem.

Psychological factors refer to such factors as the patient's dynamics, mental health history, coping strategies, and behaviors (among other variables) that influence pain and its impact. A thorough assessment will consider whether such issues as depression, anxiety, or post-traumatic stress disorder (PTSD) contribute to pain. The patient should also be assessed for the use of adaptive (e.g., exercise, yoga, meditation) vs less adaptive (e.g., bed rest, opioid analgesics) coping responses.

The psychological part of the assessment will consider dysfunctional thoughts, inactivity, and excessive pain behavior.

Social factors are a third component of a biopsychosocial approach that is important to consider. Chronic pain and suffering are often maintained in a social environment. A thorough clinical assessment will consequently identify what variables in the patient's family and close relationships may be contributing to the problem. Solicitous behavior from a well-intentioned family member often intensifies pain behavior. Similarly, socio-economic disincentives can also exacerbate pain behavior. Labor and industry payments for disability and the anticipation of a legal settlement are both potential influential factors with respect to the amount of suffering and pain behaviors the patient demonstrates.

Ericksonian Hypnosis

Ericksonian hypnosis is decidedly atheoretical. In fact, Erickson was well known for seldom, if ever, using the same technique of hypnosis for more than one patient. Like Motivational Interviewing (Rollnick et al., 2008), Erickson's techniques were based on a foundation of scientifically sound approaches, particularly social psychology (Zeig & Lankton, 1988). The range of approaches that Erickson uses are inordinately complex and expansive and are covered in multiple volumes of work (Erickson & Rossi, 1981; Erickson et al., 1976).

The induction presented in this chapter makes use of some of Erickson's more unique and better known techniques, but can hardly be purported to represent his overall approach. Erickson deemed his approach as cooperative and one in which resistance was an issue of the therapist rather than of the client. The concepts of utilization were also central to his work; the material presented by the client was used to guide therapy in virtually every case. The approaches emphasized in my intervention include truisms and forced choices. They also make use of indirect suggestions and the multiple choices that derive from those suggestions. Finally, I often use confusion and metaphors as the induction progresses.

Truisms are statements of "what is" that are difficult to argue with. Erickson used both simple and complex truisms. A simple truism might be, "You are sitting in the chair." A complex truism could be, "While your conscious mind is listening to my voice, your unconscious is hearing a message at a much deeper level." In the induction described below, I use three simple truisms and a leading statement. Thus, I might state, "You are sitting in the chair, your feet are on the floor, and you are breathing in and out... perhaps you are focusing more intently on my voice." This pattern is based on the idea of developing a "yes set" that was well established in social psychology by the time that Erickson published it. As will be illustrated, it sets up a rhythm with the patient that eventually leads to nonlinear language and mild confusion.

Indirect suggestions reduce resistance in the patient; at an overt level, they give the patient a choice. However, they are also generative in nature. Asking a patient, "I wonder how your mind will allow you to relax?", initiates a search process that generates an answer or a solution to the question, as opposed to just telling the patient to relax. Indirect suggestions also give the patient a variety of choices as to how they will respond and how they might manage their pain and suffering.

It is well established in the Motivational Interviewing literature that giving a patient two choices for behavior change will result in more compliance than giving them just one choice; giving three choices will result in even more compliance (Miller & Rollnick, 2002). Rather than tell the patient that they will experience pain relief though A, they are told that they might experience comfort from A, B, or C. This is then followed with a forced choice, such that regardless of whether they choose A, B, or C, they will experience comfort no matter what.

Confusion and metaphors were often used by Erickson to make the induction nonlinear. The thinking here is that if hypnosis can come at the patient in a haze of unpredictable suggestions, the linear cognitive processing that can thwart successful response to the clinical suggestions will be attenuated. Further, this allows the patient to hear suggestions at different levels; ideally an audio recording will be made on the patient's phone or other device and the content will be of a nature that the patient can listen to repeatedly.

Confusion can be generated by talking in non-sequential patterns, suggesting that opposites might be true, or giving multiple options (e.g., "You may feel like your pain lasts for one hour, or maybe half as long, or maybe it will be 35 and a half minutes; I do not know exactly how long your pain will last, but I do know that the time will be shorter than you expect."). Metaphors involve telling a story with an imbedded meaning. The act of telling a story further serves to make the process non-linear and difficult to track logically.

Finally, this induction makes use of dissociation. I do this by introducing the idea that there is a resource in the mind, out of which suggestions are generated. The notion is that the suggestion is coming from a dissociated part of the patient. Further, suggestions come as multiple choices from this source as described above, and will be demonstrated below.

Structure of the Induction

The following steps are involved in this induction:

1. A biopsychosocial assessment is performed on the pain problem.

2. Goals are identified for treatment. Such goals may or may not involve pain reduction and might include decreased stress, improved coping, improved sleep, more activity, altering dysfunctional thoughts, or any number of similar options.

3. Truism and forced choice induction (pacing and leading).

4. Introduction of a resource in the mind from which suggestions will come.

5. Suggestions presented in a multiple-choice fashion, including metaphors and confusion through unpredictable sequencing.

Induction Script

Clinician: OK, there are several things that you can do to manage the pain and make yourself more comfortable. Some of the goals we have identified include: making your pain less intense and bothersome; changing the automatic negative thoughts you are having; using better coping techniques, including exercising more rather than taking opioids; and improving your sleep. I would like you to start by sitting here facing me and holding eye contact with me. I know that holding eye contact can be discomforting at first, but you are free to close your eyes at any time.

You are sitting in the chair,

breathing in and out,

your feet are on the floor,

and maybe you are noticing that you are breathing more slowly and regularly.

But you are sitting in the chair,

breathing in and out,

feet are on the floor,

and maybe you are noticing how clearly you can hear my voice.

Sitting in the chair,

breathing in and out,

feet are on the floor,

and maybe your eyelids are becoming heavier.

> [This cadence and process last for roughly ten minutes. As the induction continues the clinician takes more risks with the leading statements. At first, they are safe ("breathing more slowly" or "clearly hearing my voice"). With time the clinician follows the subject's eyes and facilitates eye closure. With further time, the clinician uses intuition to make leading suggestions ("...and maybe you are having the sense of floating," or "...perhaps you are having the sense of becoming in touch with hidden resources").]

Sitting in the chair,

breathing in and out,

feet are on the floor,

and now the depth into your own internal experience is becoming profound.

Sitting in the chair,

breathing in and out,

feet are on the floor,

and now becoming aware of a profound resource in your mind.

It is that part of you that allows you to breathe without thinking about it. It is the part of you that also allows your heart to beat without willing it to do so. It is also the part of you that can be a wonderful resource if you just allow it to be.

I wonder how it will serve you now. Perhaps that resource will serve you by experiencing an interesting sensation in your lower back. It has been become filled with a cool, blue fluid.

[This analgesia/comfort imagery is continued...]

Maybe it will serve you by allowing your mind to drift off to something altogether different. I don't know. It may be that you have a profound positive image of yourself before your back was ever injured. You see yourself moving fluidly, comfortably... just loving life. And that feeling fills your entire body.

Sitting in the chair,

breathing in and out.

I have a friend that fell off a chairlift while working on it over the summer. He broke his back and was told he would never walk again. The pain was horrible. I don't know what happened over a period of time; how he was able to walk again and how his relationship with pain changed. The pain was always there for him but somehow, he just started paying attention to each moment of his life. He didn't know how he did it or how it happened. The body is remarkable that way. We can put on glasses that turn our world upside down and reverse it. Yet within a day or so we see the world normally. The mind is remarkable particularly when we can get thoughts out of the way.

Feet are on the floor.

That resource in your mind can indeed serve you in a variety of different ways. Maybe you will notice when you are having those nasty thoughts about your pain... Like, "I can't stand this pain" or "I will never be happy again." Those negative thoughts seem to appear in your darkest moments. Our thoughts just show up, even ones that are stupid.

Yet we can watch our thoughts and not be attached to them. It is as if you are lying under a freeway. Cars are passing overheard and your thoughts are going off in cars while you stay where you are. The bigger, dumber thoughts go off in trucks, you will know what they are. So much lighter without the burden of the useless thoughts...

Breathing in and out.

That resource serving you in so many ways.

And how will it be that you find yourself walking so much more with so little effort? That the desire to walk becomes an insatiable desire? So many times, the answers come to us so easily. Like trying to solve a problem and forgetting about it and, without effort, the answer is just there. That you find yourself walking every day, longer and longer distances... it becomes part of you.

[There are in infinite number of possible suggestions that can be provided at this phase and space precludes what might go

into a full induction. The suggestion phase might last 10 to 15 minutes. The main point is that the clinician addresses several domains that came out of the biopsychosocial assessment. Suggestions are offered as a series of choices in a nonlinear fashion.]

Sitting in the chair,

breathing in and out,

feet are on the floor.

Sitting in the chair,

breathing in and out,

feet are on the floor.

And maybe you will be curious about how you fall into a deep, profound, restful sleep when your head hits the pillow. That when you awaken in the night, you just focus on what you see... what you hear... and what you feel until you drift comfortably back to sleep.

[The 3-2-1 technique for sleep (e.g., Jensen, 2011) will have been taught before the induction in which the patient focuses on what they see, hear, and feel three times, twice, and then once.]

Sitting in the chair,

breathing in and out,

feet are on the floor,

and now becoming aware of the next stage of this process.

Sitting in the chair.

That the eyes opening become a signal for the hypnotic suggestions to begin folding in time.

Breathing in and out.

The eyes opening are a signal from your mind that you are safe, alert, and comfortable.

Feet are solidly on the floor.

[At this point the clinician continues the cadence until the subjects opens his or her eyes.]

Summary and Conclusions

I have hopefully provided a beginning example of the multi-layered biopsychosocial hypnotic approach to chronic pain. This was essentially the skeleton of what the true induction should be, and the clinician should enrich every element of the induction. The induction should be a creative, flexible approach by the clinician after he or she has performed a thorough evaluation and has several angles from which management can be facilitated. The induction should be audio recorded for patients, and ideally, because it is nonlinear and unpredictable, the patient will hear different suggestions each time they listen to it.

References

Erickson, M. H., & Rossi, E. L. (1981). *Experiencing hypnosis: Therapeutic approaches to altered states*. New York, NY: Irvington Publishers.

Erickson, M. H., Rossi, E. L., & Rossi, S. I. (1976). *Hypnotic realities: The induction of clinical hypnosis and forms of indirect suggestion*. New York, NY: Irvington Publishers.

Fordyce, W. E. (1976). *Behavioral methods for chronic pain and illness*. St. Louis, MO: Mosby Year Book.

Jensen, M. P. (2011). *Hypnosis for chronic pain management: Therapist guide*. New York, NY: Oxford University Press.

Miller, W. R., & Rollnick, S. (2002). *Motivational Interviewing: Preparing people for change* (2nd ed.). New York, NY: Guilford Press.

Patterson, D. R. (2010). *Clinical hypnosis for pain control.* Washington, DC: American Psychological Association.

Rollnick, S., Miller, M. R., & Butler, C. (2008). *Motivational Interviewing in health care: Helping patients change behavior.* New York, NY: Guilford.

Zeig, J., & Lankton, S. (1988). *Developing Ericksonian therapy.* Bristol, PA: Brunner/Mazel.

CHAPTER 3

Hypnosis for Managing Low Back Pain: Moving Back for the Future

Alan O. Szmelskyj

Alan Szmelskyj is an osteopath living and working in Cambridgeshire, UK. During his studies to become an osteopath in the early 1980s, he became interested in the potential of visualization and hypnosis as a means for improving pain self-management. With biopsychosocial concepts becoming an important feature of the holistic healthcare movement, he supported the idea that there should be greater prominence and integration of biopsychosocial thinking into standard osteopathic care. During the early 1990s, he began to incorporate hypnotic approaches into the management of his predominantly private-practice musculoskeletal patients. During this time, he also worked in two National Health Service occupational health roles tasked with preventing and reducing the levels of back and musculoskeletal pain. He has held academic posts at UK educational osteopathic institutions as well as board and editorial positions at two UK osteopathic journals. The University of Surrey awarded him a Psychobiology of Stress Master of Science degree, and he has an Advanced Diploma in Clinical Hypnosis and Stress Management from Staffordshire University. His master's thesis was on the interrelationship of stress, sleep, and pain in osteopathic patients. He has published a number of papers on osteopathy, musculoskeletal and back pain, and hypnosis. He is a member of the British Society of Clinical and Academic Hypnosis and is registered with the UK General Osteopathic Council. He is also a registered member of several other professional organizations. He is the senior osteopath at True Health Clinics in Cambridgeshire.

* * *

A complex and individually evolved potpourri of lifestyle and genetic factors all interact with a multitude of psychological processes to influence back pain. These factors and processes exist in the context of the person's ability to cope and to manage the demands of daily life in a society in constant flux. These, in turn, influence a person's expectations about their back pain, its causes, and its consequences (Schrooten & Linton, 2017).

Fortunately, most episodes of back pain resolve within weeks of the initial onset. However, 48% of new back pain patients will still be troubled by back pain to some extent over the following two years, with 17% developing chronic back pain (Norton et al., 2016). Our knowledge about the processes involved in the progression from acute to chronic low back pain has improved due to the pooling of cross-disciplinary constructs and empirical data (Hasenbring et al., 2012). Thus, prioritizing the management of low back pain with the objective of reducing risk of symptom escalation is an appropriate holistic goal. This goal includes maximizing both pain control and the patient's ability to function. This approach will also likely reduce the risk of disability development and will improve current and future quality of life.

Most back pain is typically classified as "non-specific;" that is, not due to any serious underlying biomedical disorder (Maher et al., 2017). Serious pathology, such as cancer, infection, or inflammatory causes occur in less than 1% of cases, and nerve root problems associated with spinal stenosis or radiculopathy account for only 10%-15% of back pain (Foster, 2011). Therefore, and not surprisingly, clinical guidelines recommend that health care providers reassure patients that most back pain is not due to serious underlying reasons (NICE, 2016; Qaseem et al., 2017).

At the individual practitioner level, taking a comprehensive history is important to identify each patient's risks for the development of chronic pain and to optimize the personalization of treatment. Taking a detailed history and a thorough clinical examination are also important in the process of reassuring patients (Holt et al., 2015).

During the initial patient evaluation, the use of appropriate communication, including hypnotic language constructs, can enhance patient-practitioner rapport. A thorough initial clinical examination can also help enhance non-specific treatment effects (Sliwinski & Elkins, 2013). Varga has noted that during an examination, "The planned use of highly complex and (to the patient) incomprehensible procedures" can itself lead to an altered state of consciousness (Varga, 2017, p. 118).

Perhaps for some individuals, this affective bridge building will form an important conduit for subsequent psycho-educational cognitive reassurance and education about pain mechanisms. This can further enhance overall treatment efficacy, reducing morbidity and improving well-being.

In my practice, which is mostly based on the management of patients with musculoskeletal pain, I have a fairly systematic framework for gathering information. Overtly, the objective of the process is to arrive at a clinical diagnosis and an understanding of what may be driving the patient's pain. Equally important, however, is the healing ritual of the approach; this I consider to be an important aspect of the non-specific but suggestive aspect of patient care.

In a paper published a couple of decades ago, I outlined how some of this thinking was applied in my osteopathic practice (Szmelskyj, 1997). Subsequently, with the advancement of knowledge in the field, I have nuanced my original musings.

There are many factors that can lead to and contribute to the development and maintenance of back pain. Some of these factors tend to play a larger role than others (Main et al., 2012). Although a detailed consideration of all of these factors is beyond the scope of this chapter, it is worthwhile to address some of those factors that may be influenced by hypnotic intervention.

Inappropriate illness beliefs of both clinicians and patients can influence back pain treatment outcomes (Setchell et al., 2017). In particular, a search—and ideally an identification of—biomechanical or structural-anatomical aetio-pathology causes for refractory pain often preoccupies patients and clinicians. The continued search for structural dysfunction may thereby act as a potential barrier for patients to acknowledge the importance of the contributing role of psychosocial factors in their experience of pain and dysfunction (Setchell et al., 2017).

Current clinical guidelines for the management of low back pain emphasize the value of activity and exercise (NICE, 2016; Airaksinen et al., 2006). Unfortunately, for some patients, fear of pain or re-injury acts as a barrier to incorporating exercise as a part of back pain self-management (Schaller et al., 2017). Fear of experiencing back pain in response to physical activity or exercise may explain, at least in part, why patient compliance with prescribed exercise is often so poor (Lin et al., 2011). This idea is consistent with research findings showing that fear avoidance beliefs are associated with poor outcomes in patients with back pain of less than six months duration (Wertli et al., 2014).

Recently it has been proposed that the usefulness of the fear avoidance model (in which pain leads to avoidance and disuse, resulting in more disability over time) for understanding the development of disabling back pain could be improved if it is used in tandem with other approaches; for example, by recognizing the cumulative load of various risk factors and better integrating the model with biological factors (Wideman et al., 2013).

Although, indirectly, it may reinforce the perception to patients that there is an underlying structural reason for their pain, encouraging patients to increase their exercise levels in order to strengthen their muscles and reduce the risk of future back injury can provide a face-valid explanation for why it would be good to engage in more activity or exercise.

Rather interestingly, and potentially of use to the hypnosis practitioner, is the ecological dimension of exercise. The context in which physical activity is undertaken appears to be an important influence on pain and behavior. For example, moderate to vigorous leisure time physical activity can help to reduce pain in patients with persistent back pain (Pinto et al., 2014). Thus, framing hypnotic suggestions for *exercise that invokes or relates to leisure time activity* may be useful for enhancing their subsequent uptake by patients.

Except for those who have the most demanding occupational physical activity levels, leisure time physical activity may also have a beneficial influence on autonomic nervous system activation (Hallman et al., 2017). The longer-term benefits of a better balance in autonomic nervous system regulation include potential reduction in cardiovascular disease risk and improvement of immune mediated inflammatory disorders. The shorter-term benefits include improvements in well-being; for example improved feelings of relaxation, calmness, and control. Practically, this suggests motivation for more leisure time physical activity engagement as a viable treatment target, both for increasing activity in general, as well as for reducing pain-related anxiety.

Using hypnosis to reduce fear avoidance and simultaneously to improve self-efficacy for physical activity may have the potential to improve physical activity levels and overall health in a cost-effective manner. Adding aspects of self-efficacy improvement and behavior change to standard physical therapy seems have such benefits (Ben-Ami et al., 2017). The overall success in encouraging patients with back pain to be more active may depend in part on current pain intensity levels, as well as on patient fear of future pain. Thus, reducing pain intensity itself is another important treatment target for improving long-term outcomes; especially given the fact that baseline pain intensity levels are predictive of back pain levels five years post pain onset (Chen et al., 2018).

Rather conveniently, pain relief is often a primary outcome in clinical trials of hypnosis in this population (e.g., Tan et al., 2010, 2015). Although methodological limitations (e.g., low sample size) of the published clinical trials evaluating the efficacy of hypnosis for back pain limits the conclusions that can be drawn from these studies, the available evidence is promising. Detailed guidance on the use of hypnosis for pain management has also been described by Mark P. Jensen in a number of publications, some of which are listed in the

Further Reading section of this chapter; many of these strategies can be adapted for the management of back pain.

In short, although the reduction of pain intensity is an appropriate and important target for treatment (hypnotic or otherwise), to focus only on this single dimension of the patient's lived-in experience is limiting. For the hypnosis practitioner, having an expanded remit of treatment targets increases the potential effectiveness of treatment.

Critical life events and the associated stress response may be an under-recognized predictor of future pain (Wippert et al., 2017). Reframing such elicited past critical life events with the patient in trance and potentially providing a safe framework in which to do so may be indicated in some instances.

Examples of other more commonly recognized treatment targets for the hypnosis practitioner include: low self-esteem, guilt, depression (Pinheiro et al., 2016), anxiety, catastrophizing, fear-avoidance, and sleep interference (Kelly et al., 2011). The specific choice and prioritization of targets for management should usually be guided by the factors that emerge during the initial evaluation, clinical triage, and shared decision-making.

By targeting self-efficacy, fear, and psychological distress (especially depression) and stress, the clinician can help prevent disability (Lee, et al., 2015). For example, when fear management and self-efficacy enhancement were added to a standard physical therapy intervention, there was less disability at 12 months, relative to physical therapy alone (Ben-Ami et al., 2017).

The factors that may be driving one patient's pain or fear of movement are likely to be quite different from the factors for another patient (Meier et al., 2018). There is not yet definitive evidence to classify fear of movement as a specific phobia (Wideman et al., 2013). However, from a therapeutic perspective, managing fear of movement as a phobia would be pragmatic. Thus, the hypnotic approaches described by Spiegel (2014) for managing specific phobias may also be appropriate for managing back pain patients' fear of movement.

Hypnosis-aided systemic desensitization, when the patient is in a sufficiently relaxed frame of mind, may be another means of reducing both the perception and the emotive response to some aspects of a patient's fear of aggravating back pain (Alladin, 2016). This may be of particular value in those instances where a patient is confident in attributing their back pain onset or aggravation as occurring in response to specific movements, certain movement patterns, or activities. This approach may also have some merit when the patient views their pain in response to the feared activity as a biomechanical failure, such as a weakness of the spine or core muscles, or a joint instability from a degenerative process. Using hypnotic age regression (see example script later in this chapter) might be useful in reframing the perception of some of these feared scenarios. This may be achieved by using elements of what Alladin described as "Syncratic cognition-Syncratic response" (Alladin, 2016).

When using this approach, I initially utilize cognitively orientated pain science education and positive reinforcement, as well as explaining good ergonomic principles, as a positive coping technique to enable the patient to understand and manage some of the feared activities. Often, I demonstrate to the patient specific ways to perform the feared activity in a safe way, effectively providing the patient with a "live" context-sensitive action observation(s) experience.

For example, I might demonstrate how cleaning a bathtub need not involve an over-stretching flexion action of the back. During the process of demonstrating how to do this task safely, the language use would typically include positive suggestions. For example,

So, although in the past you might have been a bit scared of bending to clean your bathtub, you can see how when you bend down to clean your bathtub, you can *do it quite safely and your back will be perfectly fine.*

This language use might be viewed as indirectly reinforcing a negative belief in the patient that a forward-flexion movement process is harmful. However, the benefits of enhancing patient self-efficacy, by enabling the patient to be able to engage in important activities of daily living safely, is arguably more empowering to their independence and quality of life.

If the patient still lacks confidence with undertaking bathtub cleaning tasks, and keeping this example going, I might then use a motor imagery approach to boost confidence further. To help the patient understand motor imagery, I might use the metaphor of mental training to enhance athletic performance:

So, if we pretend or imagine that you are an athlete, and put yourself in the athlete's shoes, then you would want to do anything that's legal and ethical to be the best in class in your sporting activity, would you not? *[Wait for patient to show agreement.]*

As you may know, many highly successful athletes *[if the patient is a golf follower, for example, I would mention Jack Nicklaus, or I might generalize and say many members of sports teams regularly use mental practice]* **have achieved excellence in**

their field by mentally rehearsing, many times over, their shots, their strokes, repeatedly mentally practicing the way they move... to get better at doing what they need to do with their bodies in whatever context or situation they find themselves.

Thus, following on from an induction, deepening and establishment of a safe place (or sometimes safe places so that they can move in between, to and from, and do different activities in different places), the patient would be invited to visualize undertaking the particularly feared movement or task. This would be done in a stepwise, graded way with repetition to reinforce confidence, emphasizing more of a kinesthetic imagery and fluctuating from first to third person observer perspective in the process. The patient might also be invited to visualize themselves undertaking the feared movement from the perspective of a significant other.

There is emerging evidence that using motor imagery with the patient in trance may help to integrate, via thalamic involvement, the attention system modulated by the hypnotic state and the motor control system engaged in motor imagery (Müller et al., 2013). Potentially, using motor imagery in hypnosis may be beneficial for patients with chronic low back pain who may struggle to perform motor imagery out of hypnosis because of reduced activity in the sensory-motor areas and reduced functional connectivity (Vrana et al., 2015).

Elements of the Consultation Process Prior to Formal Induction

From the moment I first greet the patient in the reception room, I observe him or her and watch how he or she moves. This helps me to establish a snapshot of the patient's immediate pain and disability level. Once we are in the consultation room, I invite the patient to sit, remain standing, move around, or lie down. After initial rapport establishment, the consultation proceeds and would typically aim to obtain information regarding the following elements:

- Psychosocial-occupational background
- Pain complaint presentation
- Pain attributions, health beliefs
- Ergonomic/biomechanical factors
- Health and illness history
- Resilience and coping strategies

My clinical examination focuses on undertaking a systematic, detailed musculoskeletal examination and identifying physiological/functional dysfunction. The extensiveness and complexity of this process is such that it potentially acts as a ritualistic trance-inducing process, as well as providing enhanced patient reassurance when positive suggestions are used; therefore, perhaps non-specifically adding to the patient's expectancy of an improved outcome. Triage would include examination of the articular and soft tissue states of all lower extremity joints as well as a detailed spinal articular and soft tissue functional assessment. Usually this is integrated with full peripheral nervous system examination, observation of the patient demonstrating their typical occupational postures, and discussion of the relevant ergonomic principles.

Diagnostic Reassurance, Cognitive Education, and Prognosis Mapping

After I elicit the background information and perform the physical examination, I summarize the salient points of the findings. At this point, I also typically explain how biomechanical, postural/ergonomic, socio-occupational, and neurophysiological processes or factors may be contributing to, or have previously contributed to, their current pain and disability. At this stage I would mention the relevance of any psychological and physical co-morbidities relevant to the timescale of their rehabilitation and recovery.

As a part of this process, I explain neurophysiological pain concepts, often guiding them to appropriate third-party resources (for example, Butler and Mosely's *Explain Pain* and Haines' *Pain is Really Strange*) and raise the issue of pain being a potential physical and psychological stressor that "winds up" patients' pain responses.

This often leads into a discussion of how to mobilize relaxation responses to achieve pain relief. During this stage, I may also use some hypnotically framed language and suggestions, particularly encouraging the patient to visualize a life with reduced pain awareness and more satisfying activity. The therapeutic intent is to guide the patient to better understand the processes of quality of life restoration, as well as exploring how pain improvement might be achievable; assuming that no underlying biomedical/pathological reason for the patient's pain is identified.

Pre-Hypnosis Ecological Checks

Before starting a formal hypnosis session, I invite the patient to choose how he or she would like to position him or herself (e.g., recumbent, sitting), and I ensure that the patient understands that he or she can alter the position as needed during the hypnosis session. Earlier in the consultation, I would have also sought to identify any potential environmental abreaction phobias, such as fear of water or of flying, that could emerge during the hypnotic processes. With the following script it is also useful to know if the patient has had a history of any form of abuse that could potentially intrude into an age-regression experience.

The approach also assumes that fear avoidance is a form of phobic responding and hence the ideas outlined by David Spiegel (Spiegel, 2014) underlie the thinking behind the script. The words or phrases in parentheses may be used when the practitioner feels they are appropriate.

Example Script:
Moving Back for the Future

Clinician: As you let yourself get as comfortable as you can, take in a slow deep breath, or two, or maybe even three. ... With each breath you take, if you want, you can take slightly longer to breathe in, and then to breathe out. Allowing yourself to feel more at ease with each breath you take into your body. Allowing yourself to feel more comfortable and relaxed as you breathe out.

[Fractionation with possible confusion.]

(Imagine how it feels) As (if) I put my hand gently on your back, you may feel the warmth of my hand on the muscles of your back. You may find the gentle relaxing pressure (touch) and the heat from the palm may give you a comforting (perhaps even a healing) feeling in your back; a feeling that you may have been missing for a while.

Your pain will ease, as you let your back relax, becoming loose. If you would like to, then you can, with each breath, or two, or three, you can choose to allow yourself to ignore any unpleasant sensations or tenderness, any sensations that interfere with your letting your back feel relaxed and comfortable.

[Fractionation, deepening of trance induction, may be possible if the patient chooses to count the breaths.]

With each slow, deep breath in, and out, you can let the relaxation grow and spread, just as much as you want to, but no more than you need to... to release, allowing your back to adjust itself, to free itself of any inconvenient experience it's been involved with.

[If there has been gross over-protection/spasm in response to movement, the patient may not be confident about allowing their back to be totally relaxed; they have the choice to relax to whatever level they feel comfortable. Also, a suggestion for self-adjustment may fit with the belief model of the patient.]

You can, if you wish, allow your back, deep down inside, to become more comfortable and at ease, and allow that relaxed feeling to allow the blood to flow into the muscles, joints, and discs, bringing the nutrients and energy it (your body/your back) needs to heal much faster and much better than it has before, allowing it to be less stressed and tense and instead be much more relaxed, and much stronger, more free and flexible, and more happy and content and at the same time allowing it to become more full of energy each time, as you move the back.

[Acknowledging emotive aspects of the back pain and giving permission for the potential healing precursors to be invoked.]

Feel the freedom, the ease, as you see yourself allowing your back to gently move forwards and backwards. Then allow yourself to see your body and your back move gently side to side; all the while feeling in control of your body. Noticing how normally, how comfortably it moves. Seeing and feeling the ease of movement may even be a very pleasant surprise. Not surprisingly, with this more comfortable feeling of motion in your back, you may want to test it out, just a little bit. Just to see how strong and stable it feels. You may want to allow yourself now, and in the future, to walk just a little bit more, a little bit more than you used to.

[Post-hypnotic suggestion to walk more.]

Seeing yourself moving confidently, heading towards where you want to go, your thoughts wandering to where you want to be. Seeing yourself stepping over the things that may be in the way, gliding through and past obstacles that used to stop you moving onwards, achieving what you need to achieve. Doing what you really want to enjoy doing.

(Now), there may be tiny stumbles or minor trips as you move about; that is natural. As you look for meaning in these, you find that you smile deep down inside, as you realize they mean no more now than when as a little child you took your first steps, when you knew it was the right time to stop sitting and crawling around and to start exploring the world. With this simple and fresh realization, you now know and understand that there isn't as much to fear as you first thought.

[Metaphor/suggestion to not be over-thinking/analyzing any minor movement-related discomfort.]

As you look back, far enough in time, to when you were much more mobile, maybe even to a time when you were much younger, take yourself to some special or favorite places—places where you see and feel yourself being safe and secure, and see yourself enjoying moving around. (You may want to put yourself back inside the body and mind of when you were that fearless child. If so, then allow yourself to step inside, and see things through the eyes of yourself as a child.) See things from the eyes of *[patient's name]*.

Perhaps you can let me know when you are there by taking a couple of big but slow, deep breaths.

[Age regression to childhood.]

Are you comfortable, here and now? Perhaps you want to gently allow the head to nod a couple of times to let me know that you are comfortable.

You can, if you want to, tell me how old as a child or adolescent you might be now, or you can show me your age by raising the fingers on your hands.

[Ecological testing of age-regressed state. Wait for the patient to acknowledge comfort, be mindful of abreaction if the patient has not disclosed past childhood trauma/abuse.]

So maybe, if you want to, you can go to a really good place, a fun place, where you can really enjoy yourself, to where no one or nothing can scare you or hurt you, a really fun safe and special place. Maybe you might choose to stroll there, or quickly walk there, maybe you want to scoot or bike there, or maybe jog or run there, perhaps you maybe even want to swim there, or swim when you are there.

Now, allow yourself to experience and enjoy the *movement* and mobility of being a carefree child, because as you do, you realize that you can do more and go further and quicker than ever before; finding and *fearlessly* exploring and *enjoying* all the things *you can do*. Perhaps you might want to go...

[Italicized for emphasis, suggestions made for activities done using potentially feared body actions, but also invoking curiosity.]

(Clambering over and under and around the bed)

(Jumping and bouncing off furniture like a jack-in-the-box)

(Crouching down, and lifting things up, curious to see what's underneath)

And then effortlessly standing up, moving your weight onto the front of your feet; then stretching and straightening up, allowing your body, and feel your body reaching its full height. Allowing you to reach the things that were once out of your grasp.

[Reaching/stretching movements emphasized.]

Moving outside, the great pleasure and fun you feel as under your own control... you can run and run without needing a break, full of energy and life. Climbing up the stairs, up to the top of a slide, easily sitting at the top and letting go of the sides, experiencing the exhilaration as you whizz down, quickly getting up and running around for another go, and then another and another.

[More rapid movement and ease of sitting emphasized.]

Before you know it, without even thinking about it, you soon realize, as you get more confident and more skilled on the gentler slides, that even the scariest looking slide isn't scary at all.

(As time goes by) you mature and you grow older, bigger, and stronger... becoming wiser, finding yourself moving more easily and confidently. Effortlessly walking, balancing on the edge of a curb, until you wobble and then with a slight and easy readjustment of your body posture you quickly regain control of your balance and carry on.

[Ease of movement and ease of responding and adapting to perturbations of movement emphasized.]

Soon you find yourself moving and interacting, having fun in the company of others, perhaps playing playground games, or maybe you're in school PE lessons, or in drama class, or dancing at the end-of-term or semester party or disco.

[Fun and enjoyment of social engagement is emphasized. Here, any specific situations that were shared by the patient during the information elicitation of fun times in childhood, or of events that the patient is particularly proud of as childhood or adolescent achievement, could be woven into the script; for example, a birthday party, a sporting success, a performing arts performance; any of these could enhance the emotional enjoyment of doing things.]

So now, and in the future, the unpredictability of how, or when, or why, you move brings you greater and greater confidence as you tackle all types of physical exertion with lasting comfort.

[Post-hypnotic suggestions to feel confident in the face of the unpredictability of movement. For the patient who appears to be disassociated from their back, the following phraseology may be used.]

So now you know, and your back knows, that in the future the unpredictability of how, or when, or why, you move and your back (and the (hip/leg/body part[s]) moves, it now feels comfortable to you. As you confidently tackle all types of physical exertion with ease and lasting comfort; with increasing levels of ease and comfort. You may also find the body and body parts seem to understand and communicate with each other much better than before.

[Then allow the patient the opportunity to spend some time re-exploring, re-experiencing, and doing some of the things they enjoyed before re-orientating to the here and now.]

So, you can now allow yourself a little while to do, in whatever safe place you need to be in, whatever you need to do to get even better; to get more comfortable and more confident doing what you have to do now and in the future.

Now, see yourself moving back into the future, see yourself back in the future freely doing what you really want to do, see how good that feels deep down inside.

Perhaps you can see how the whole of your body moves easily, without any effort or need for you to think about how it moves. As you move, your back and your spine move smoothly back in line and in rhythm and in time. Your spine resonates with the rest of your body like a new, (classical) finely tuned instrument.

[Suggestions to experience future confidence in the back.]

And enjoy how much better and more confident and comfortable you've become at doing what you want to do and need to do.

[Open-ended invitation to enhance self-confidence, self-esteem, and control.]

Perhaps you feel ready now, or will be ready very soon, to confidently experience playing the beginnings of a new tune and to move in time with the music.

When you get home tonight, and whenever you are falling asleep in bed, you'll find you can allow the body and the muscle's memory to remember how good it feels to do the things you did today.

And if you find you have a little time in bed before you fall asleep, or if you wake up and need to fill in the time before you move back into a deep, restful sleep, you can also practice/rehearse and re-master those actions and activities that will be most useful to you tomorrow, to do whatever you need to do, whenever you need to do them.

So, when you are ready to do so, you can take a slow and deep comfortable breath in, and then slowly breathe out, and at the same time as slowly breathing out you can count down three, two, one, and you can open your eyes.

References

Airaksinen, O., Brox, J. I., Cedraschi, C., Hildbrandt, J., Klaber-Moffett, J., Kovacs, F., ... Zanoli, G. (2006). Chapter 4. COST B13 Working group on guidelines for the management of chronic nonspecific low back pain. *European Spine Journal, 15, Supplement 2*, s192-s300.

Alladin, A. (2016). Cognitive hypnotherapy. In G. R. Elkins (Ed.) *Handbook of medical and psychological hypnosis: Foundations, applications, and professional issues* (pp. 99-117). New York, NY: Springer.

Ben-Ami, N., Chodick, G., Mirovsky, Y., Pincus, T., & Shapiro, Y. (2017). Increasing recreational physical activity in patients with chronic low back pain: A pragmatic controlled clinical trial. *Journal of Orthopaedic & Sports Physical Therapy, 47*, 57–66.

Chen, Y., Campbell, P., Strauss, V. Y., Foster, N. E., Jordan, K. P., & Dunn, K. M. (2018). Trajectories and predictors of the long-term course of low back pain: Cohort study with 5-year follow-up. *Pain, 159,* 252-260.

Foster, N. E. (2011). Barriers and progress in the treatment of low back pain. *BMC Medicine, 9,* 108.

Hallman, D. M., Jorgensen, M., & Holtermann, A. (2017). On the health paradox of occupational and leisure-time physical activity using objective measurements: Effects on autonomic imbalance. *PLoS One, 12,* e0177042.

Hasenbring, M. I., Rusu, A. C., & Turk D. C. (2012). *From acute to chronic back pain: Risk factors, mechanisms, and clinical implications.* New York, NY: Oxford University Press.

Holt, N., Pincus, T., & Vogel, S. (2015). Reassurance during low back pain consultations with GPs: A qualitative study. *British Journal of General Practice, 639,* e692-701.

Kelly, G. A., Blake, C., Power, C. K., O'keeffe, D., & Fullen, B. M. (2011). The association between chronic low back pain and sleep: A systematic review. *Clinical Journal of Pain, 27,* 169-181.

Lee, H., Hubscher, M., Moseley, G. L., Kamper, S. J., Traeger, A. C., Mansell, G., & McAuley, J. H. (2015). How does pain lead to disability? A systematic review and meta-analysis of mediation studies in people with back and neck pain. *Pain, 156,* 988-997.

Lin, C. W., McAuley, J. H., Macedo, L. G., Barnett, D. C., Smeets, R. J., & Verbunt, J. A. (2011). Relationship between physical activity and disability in low back pain: A systematic review and meta-analysis. *Pain, 152,* 607-613.

Maher, C., Underwood, M., & Buchbinder, R. (2017). Non-specific low back pain. *The Lancet, 389,* 736-747.

Main, C. J., Kendall, N. A. S., & Hasenbring, M. I. (2012). Screening of psychosocial risk factors (yellow flags) for chronic back pain and disability. In M. I. Hasenbring, A. C. Rusu, & D. C. Turk (Eds.), *From acute to chronic back pain:*

Risk factors, mechanisms, and clinical implications (pp. 203-229). New York, NY: Oxford University Press.

Meier, M. L., Humphreys, B. K., Vrana, A., Seifritz, E., Stampfli, P., & Schweinhardt, P. (2018). Pain-related fear: Dissociable neural sources of different fear constructs. *eNeuro, 5,* ENEURO.0107-18.2018.

Müller, M., Bacht, B., Prochnow, D., Schramm, S., & Seitz, R. J. (2013). Activation of thalamus in motor imagery results from gating by hypnosis. *Neuroimage, 6,* 361-367.

National Institute for Health and Care Excellence. (2016). *Low back pain and sciatica in over 16s: Assessment and management* (NICE guideline NG59). www.nice.org.uk/guidance/ng59.

Norton, G., McDonough, C. M., Cabral, H. J., Schwartz, M., & Burgess, J. F. (2016). Classification of patients with incident non-specific low back pain: Implications for research. *The Spine Journal, 16,* 567–576.

Pinheiro, M. B., Ferreira, M. L., Refshauge, K., Maher, C. G., Ordonana, J. R., Andrade, T. B., ... Ferreira, P. H. (2016). Symptoms of depression as a prognostic factor for low back pain: A systematic review. *The Spine Journal, 16,* 105-116.

Pinto, R., Ferreira, P., Kongsted, A., Ferreira, M., Maher, C., & Kent, P. (2014). Self-reported moderate-to-vigorous leisure time physical activity predicts less pain and disability over 12 months in chronic and persistent low back pain. *European Journal of Pain, 18,* 1190-1198.

Qaseem, A., Wilt, T. J., McLean, R. M., & Forciea, M. A. (2017). Noninvasive treatments for acute, subacute, and chronic low back pain: A clinical practice guideline from the American College of Physicians. *Annals of Internal Medicine, 166,* 514-530.

Schaller, A., Exner, A. K., Schroeer, S., Kleineke, V., & Sauzet, O. (2017). Barriers to physical activity in low back pain patients following rehabilitation: A secondary analysis of a randomized controlled trial. *BioMed Research International,* 6925079.

Schrooten, M. G. S., & Linton, S. J. (2017). Changing pain expectations: The role of social context and communication. *Pain, 58,* 1185-1186.

Setchell, J., Costa N., Ferreira, M., Makovey, J., Nielson, M., & Hodges, P. W. (2017). Individuals' explanations for their persistent or recurrent low back pain: A cross-sectional survey. *BMC Musculoskeletal Disorders, 18,* 466.

Sliwinski, J., & Elkins, G .R. (2013). Enhancing placebo effects: Insights from social psychology. *American Journal of Clinical Hypnosis, 55,* 236-248.

Spiegel, S. B. (2014). Current issues in the treatment of specific phobia: Recommendations for innovative applications of hypnosis. *American Journal of Clinical Hypnosis, 56,* 389-404.

Szmelskyj, A. O. (1997). Psycho-social and hypnotic theories of osteopathy and therapeutic applications. *Journal of Osteopathic Education and Clinical Practice, 7,* 32-40.

Tan, G., Fukui, T., Jensen, M. P., Thornby, J., & Waldman, K. L. (2010). Hypnosis treatment for chronic low back pain. *International Journal of clinical and Experimental Hypnosis, 58,* 53-68.

Tan, G., Rintala, D. H., Jensen, M. P., Fukui, T., Smith, D., & Williams, W. (2015). A randomized controlled trial of hypnosis compared with biofeedback for adults with chronic low back pain. *European Journal of Pain, 19,* 271-280.

Varga, K. (2017). Suggestive techniques without inductions for medical interventions In M.P. Jensen (Ed.) *The art and practice of hypnotic induction: Favorite methods of master clinicians* (pp. 114-135). Kirkland, WA: Denny Creek Press.

Vrana, A., Hotz-Boendermaker, S., Stämpfli, P., Hänggi, J., Seifritz, E., Humphreys, B. K., & Meier, M. L. (2015).

Differential neural processing during motor imagery of daily activities in chronic low back pain patients. *PLoS ONE, 10*, e0142391.

Wideman, T. H., Asmundson, G. G. J., Smeets, R. J. E. M., Zautra, A. J., Simmonds, M. J., Sullivan, M. J. L., … Edwards, R. R. (2013). Rethinking the fear avoidance model: Toward a multidimensional framework of pain-related disability. *Pain, 154*, 2262-2265.

Wertli, M. M., Rasmussen-Barr, E., Held, U., Weiser, S., Bachmann, L. M., & Brunner, F. (2014). Fear-avoidance beliefs-a moderator of treatment efficacy in patients with low back pain: A systematic review. *The Spine Journal, 14*, 2658-2678.

Wippert, P. M., Fliesser, M., & Krause, M. (2017). Risk and protective factors in the clinical rehabilitation of chronic back pain. *Journal of Pain Research, 10*, 1569–1579.

For Further Reading

Butler, D. S., & Moseley, G. L. (2013). *Explain pain* (2nd Ed). Adelaide, Australia: Noigroup.

Haines, S. (2015). *Pain is really strange*. London, United Kingdom: Singing Dragon.

Jensen, M. P. (2011). *Hypnosis for chronic pain management: Therapist Guide*. New York, NY: Oxford University Press.

Jensen, M. P., & Patterson, D. R. (2008). Hypnosis in the relief of pain and pain disorders. In M. R. Nash & A. J. Barnier (Eds.), *The Oxford handbook of hypnosis: Theory, research and practice* (pp. 502-533). New York, NY: Oxford University Press.

Jensen, M. P. (Ed.) (2017). *The art and practice of hypnotic induction: Favorite methods of master clinicians*. Kirkland, WA: Denny Creek Press.

CHAPTER 4

Hypnotherapy for Fibromyalgia

Giuseppe De Benedittis

Giuseppe De Benedittis is an Associate Professor of Neurosurgery at the University of Milan. He founded and directed the Interdepartmental Center for the Study and Treatment of Pain at the University of Milan, the first multidisciplinary pain center established in Italy. He is internationally recognized as one of the leading experts in pain therapy, in particular in the field of primary chronic headaches, orofacial pain, pain in the spine (neck pain, low back pain), neuropathic pain (e.g., shingles), fibromyalgia, and cancer pain. His long clinical experience and his experimental studies have focused on the measurement of pain, quality of life, the psychological aspects of chronic pain, and the use of innovative techniques for pain control (pharmacological, anesthesiological, psychophysiological) in a multidisciplinary approach, which takes into account all of the most relevant components of chronic pain. Professor De Benedittis has also been a recognized pioneer in the clinical and experimental use of hypnosis for pain control, contributing to the elucidation of the complex neurophysiological mechanisms of hypnotic analgesia. He is Vice President of the Italian Society of Hypnosis and is a Member of the Board of the International Society of Hypnosis. He received the Ernest R. Hilgard Award for Scientific Excellence from the International Society for Hypnosis in 2009.

* * *

Fibromyalgia syndrome (FMS) is a heterogeneous, complex, debilitating, and functional pain syndrome characterized by chronic, intolerable musculoskeletal widespread pain (i.e., pain in the axial skeleton and on both sides of the body, above and below the waist). It is pain that has lasted for three months or longer and is associated with hyperalgesia, likely due to central hyperexcitability and loss of descending inhibition (De Benedittis, 2016; Wolfe et al., 1990). In addition to chronic widespread pain, other key symptoms are fatigue, non-restorative sleep, cognitive/emotional dysfunction, and compromised health-related quality of life (HRQoL; De Benedittis, 2012, 2016).

Epidemiology

Fibromyalgia syndrome affects 3%-5% of the general population in Europe, occurs mostly in women of middle or older age and lower socioeconomic status (Whibley et al., 2016), and generates considerable economic, social, and personal costs (Lami et al., 2013). A dramatic increase in the incidence of patients with FMS has been recently reported, with a striking female prevalence (85%) (De Benedittis & Malafronte, 2014). A few cases of FMS in children have also been observed (De Benedittis, unpublished).

Pathophysiology

Pathogenesis of FMS remains poorly understood. Despite widespread somatic symptoms and signs, including pain and multiple trigger points, evidence for peripheral (e.g., musculoskeletal) dysfunction is lacking. However, an increasing body of evidence supports the notion of a complex, central dysfunctional pain syndrome with hyperalgesia, likely due to central hyperexcitability and loss of descending inhibition, as structural brain changes and neurocognitive impairment suggest (De Benedittis, 2012, 2014, 2016).

Neuroimaging studies

Recent neuroimaging studies have shown accelerated brain gray matter loss in patients with FMS as compared with healthy controls, suggesting a premature aging of the brain in individuals with FMS (Kuchinad, et al., 2007). Possible explanations for the decreased gray matter density in these disorders might include different mechanisms which are not mutually exclusive. For example: (1) chronic nociceptive input; (2) effect of chronic psychosocial stressors; (3) cytochemic excitotoxicity (i.e., atrophy secondary to excitotoxicity and/or exposure to inflammation-related agents, such as cytokines); (4) maladaptive allocation of attentional resources in anticipating/amplifying the nociceptive input ("overuse atrophy"); and (5) predisposing central sensitization factors (De Benedittis, 2012, 2016).

A number of brain imaging studies have reported an increased activation of the pain processing network in fibromyalgia patients (as compared with healthy controls) in response to nociceptive stimuli, implying the presence of a hyperactive pain detection and processing system (Schmidt-Wilcke & Diers, 2017).

Other studies provide evidence that FMS patients display reduced activation or connectivity within the pain inhibitory network (Schmidt-Wilcke & Diers, 2017). It has been shown that hyperconnectivity of the insular cortex to other components of the pain processing network and other networks involved in self-awareness and self-monitoring (i.e., the default mode network) makes the brain more vulnerable to increased pain perception and the development of a chronic pain state (Schmidt-Wilcke & Diers, 2017).

FMS, Abuse, and Posttraumatic Stress Disorder (PTSD)

Developmental adverse life events such as emotional, physical, and sexual abuse have been discussed as potential etiologic factors in FMS (e.g., De Benedittis, 2016; Varinen et al., 2017). The trauma hypothesis of FMS assumes a link between these types of abuse and potential pathophysiologic mechanisms of FMS, such as perturbed neuroprocessing of grievous stimuli or hyporeactivity of the hypothalamic-pituitary-adrenal gland axis (De Benedittis, 2016).

Controlled studies and meta-analyses have shown a striking prevalence of physical and sexual abuse in patients with FMS as compared with healthy controls (Häuser et al., 2011; Paras et al., 2009; Walker et al., 1997). Furthermore, abuse history in patients with FMS was found to be associated with worse symptoms and quality of life (HRQoL) compared with those patients without abuse history (Jiao et al., 2015).

A recent study by Häuser et al. (2013) in a population of 395 consecutive patients found a 45% incidence of PTSD in patients with FMS, as compared to only a 3% incidence in the healthy controls. In more than two-thirds of the cases, adverse events antedated the onset of FMS; in less than one-third of the cases, these events followed the onset of FMS, with adverse events occurring in the same year of FMS in 4% of the cases. Conversely, over half of the sample (n = 76) of female veterans with PTSD who had been deployed in the Gulf-War had a positive FMS screening score (D'Aoust et al., 2017).

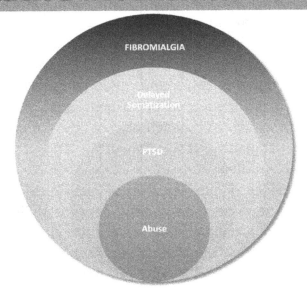

Figure 4.1. Putative mechanisms of Fibromyalgia.

What is the link between FMS, abuse, and PTSD? A recent study (De Benedittis, 2014) tried to solve the FMS conundrum, testing whether adverse childhood events (ACE) acted as early stressors for delayed, somatized PTSD, being, as such, antecedents or precursors of FMS. Thirty-eight patients with FMS were compared with patients with nonspecific chronic low back pain (NS-CLBP), matched for age, sex, pain duration, and severity. The results of this study showed that patients with FMS reported a significantly higher percentage of multiple ACE on the ACE scale (Felitti et al., 1998) as compared with the NS-CLBP group. As far as the type of abuse, patients with FMS had a significantly higher percentage of physical, sexual, and emotional abuse, and, though to a lesser extent, neglect. Concomitantly, patients with FMS scored significantly higher than NS-CLBP in the posttraumatic severity symptom scale (Foa et al., 1997). The conclusions of the study suggest that developmental abuse might induce a PTSD with delayed somatization, eventually leading to FMS (Figure 1). Is this *really* the missing link? As of yet, we do not know; further longitudinal studies are needed to solve this intriguing puzzle.

Diagnosis

Diagnosis and management of FMS remain a challenge for patients and healthcare professionals. It often takes more than two years for a diagnosis to be made after the initial onset of pain. Referral to specialists and investigations result in high healthcare use for up to 10 years prior to diagnosis, compared with persons who do not have FMS (Macfarlane et al., 2017).

In 2016, Wolfe and colleagues (Wolfe et al., 2016) developed the following diagnostic criteria for FMS, now used by the majority of practitioners in the field:

1. Generalized pain, defined as pain in at least 4 of 5 regions excluding the jaw, chest, and abdomen, is present.

2. Symptoms have been present at a similar level for at least 3 months.

3. Widespread pain index (WPI; a measure of the number of painful body regions) ≥ 7 and symptom severity scale (SSS) score ≥ 5 or WPI of 4–6 and SSS score ≥ 9.

4. A diagnosis of fibromyalgia is valid irrespective of other diagnoses. A diagnosis of fibromyalgia does not exclude the presence of other clinically important illnesses.

Treatment

Given the heterogeneous symptomatology and complex pathophysiological mechanisms involved in the genesis and maintenance of FMS, and considering the biopsychosocial model in understanding the pain experience, it is not surprising that multimodal and multidisciplinary approaches have been widely advocated (De Benedittis, 2016). Evidence-based treatment guidelines mostly recommend multimodal approaches that include pharmacological treatment, physical exercise, and psychological treatments (Macfarlane et al., 2017).

However, there is still no consensus among the international guidelines for FMS treatment, probably because of the methodological heterogeneity of research studies and the broad symptomatic spectrum of FMS patients (Talotta et al., 2017).

Among psychological interventions, cognitive behavioral therapy (CBT), alone and/or in combination with pharmacological treatment and other psychological interventions (e.g., imagery/hypnosis) is the most commonly used treatment (Lami et al., 2013). Moreover, along with exercise, CBT has received the highest rating for level of evidence in a synthesis of clinical guidelines (Whibley et al., 2016). A meta-analysis of 23 randomized controlled trials (RCTs) investigated the impact of CBT on pain, function, and mood in individuals with FMS (Bernardy et al., 2013). Positive, yet modest, effects were observed both at the end of treatment and in the longer term for all outcomes.

In a context of public health systems, it is crucial to evaluate the cost benefit of treatment. Therefore, there is a need for more controlled studies of treatment effectiveness that meet the standard methodological requirements. More research is also needed to identify moderating and mediating variables that lead to a suitable match between the psychological characteristics of patients and treatment (Lami et al., 2013).

Hypnotherapy for the Management of FMS

Management of FMS may be challenging, as it seems to be refractory to most treatments. Hypnosis used alone, as well as in combination with other treatments, has been shown to be effective in the control of chronic pain of various origins (De Benedittis, 2016; Jensen, 2016).

A few case studies and controlled trials of patients with FMS support the potential efficacy of hypnosis for this condition (e.g., Bernardy et al., 2011; Haanen et al., 1991; Martínez-Valero et al., 2008; Picard et al., 2013; but see Castel et al., 2007, for a null finding).

In 2009, Thieme and Gracely published a meta-analysis on the efficacy of psychological treatments (including five RCTs with hypnotherapy) showing mild effects of hypnosis. A meta-analysis by Bernardy et al., (2011) reviewed six RCTs including 256 FMS cases with a follow-up of eight weeks (average), showing a large effect on pain relief and a medium effect on sleep, whereas HRQoL remained unchanged (see also Zech et al., 2017).

A more recent RCT (De Benedittis, 2012, 2014) included 24 consecutive patients with a diagnosis of FMS. Owing to ethical reasons, a placebo-controlled study was not feasible. Patients were randomly assigned to hypnotherapy plus standard pharmacological treatment (n = 12; H group) or purely standard pharmacological treatment as controls (n = 12; C group). Follow-up evaluations were at Month 3 (M3) and Month 6 (M6). Our primary outcome was pain relief, as measured by means of a visual analog scale and numerical rating scale. Secondary outcomes included HRQoL, energy (or fatigue reduction), and sleep. Mean pain relief was 61% in the H group and 53% in the C group. The difference was not statistically significant. Long-term (M6) mean pain relief for H and C patients was 70% and 25%, respectively (p = .001). Moreover, in the long run, hypnosis proved to be significantly superior to standard treatment as far as QoL, energy, and restorative sleep were concerned. Patients' satisfaction after treatment was significantly higher in the H group (75%) as opposed to the C group (37%). Continued home practice coupled with periodic "booster" sessions possibly accounted for maintenance of gains. Safety of hypnotic treatment was excellent, with no reports of adverse events related to hypnosis/self-hypnosis.

In conclusion, hypnosis may be a useful adjunct tool to manage chronic pain and dysfunctional symptoms in patients with FMS. A far greater population of patients, trials of higher quality, and further research are still needed to establish the efficacy of hypnotherapy in FMS.

Hypnotic Treatment Protocol

FMS patients usually receive one weekly hypnotic session for the first three months, with two monthly sessions for the next three months; about 14 sessions in all. Patients are instructed to practice self-hypnosis twice daily (approximately 20 minutes per session).

As far as hypnotic procedures are concerned, following standard trance induction by eye fixation, deepening of hypnosis is achieved with suggestions for multisensory imagery and progressive relaxation. Subsequently, indirect (Ericksonian) suggestions are given as target suggestions for cognitive modulation of pain in an individualized form. These include (De Benedittis, 2016): (1) dissociation ("Pain does not belong to you"); (2) imagining swimming in a magic swimming pool; (3) respiratory pacing (slow breathing, shown to be effective in reducing pain); (4) age progression (projecting to a pain-free future); and (5) partial posthypnotic amnesia for the pain experience.

Some other, rather innovative hypnotherapeutic methods have been used in selected cases. Algovisual synaesthesia (De Benedittis, 2001) has been successfully applied to patients with FMS. The rationale is to cognitively modulate pain by multisensory cross talk. In one case, the patient with FMS was asked, during trance, to associate her pain experience with a color. The starting color was a pink. Subsequently, the patient was asked to associate another color with the experience of well-being. In this case, the ending color was a white, marble color. In the following hypnotic session, suggestions were given to trance-form the starting pink-rose color into the ending white-marble color, thereby resulting in significant pain relief without even mentioning the term pain. In another case, a patient was asked to trance-form the starting deep-blue color, associated with pain, into the ending sky-blue color, associated with the sense of well-being, resulting in significant pain relief.

Finally, in selected cases of highly hypnotizable subjects with a clear history of abuse and PTSD, hypnoanalytical treatment has been successful. Unconscious trauma and conflicts were unveiled by age regression and worked through. This eventually led to (almost complete) symptom resolution.

Two primary induction procedures for the management of FMS are presented in this section:

1. Rapid Induction Fibromyalgia Relief (RIFR); and

2. The Space Journey.

Rapid Induction Fibromyalgia Relief (RIFR)

This induction procedure focuses upon the following: (1) progressive relaxation, (2) deepening trance, (3) a secret and safe place, (4) synesthesia suggestions, (5) cognitive restructuring, (6) supporting self-esteem and a positive body image, (7) reducing fatigue, and (8) post-hypnotic amnesia.

Clinician: I'd like to talk with you for a moment to see if you'd like to feel more comfortable and relaxed than you might expect. OK, then... the best way to begin feeling more comfortable is to just begin by sitting as comfortably as you can right now... go ahead and adjust yourself to the most comfortable position you like... that's fine. Now, you may want to close your eyes and keep them closed to feel more comfortable. Take one very big, satisfying, deep breath. That's fine. You may already notice how good that feels... how warm your neck and shoulders can feel. ... Now, I'd like you to take four more very deep, very comfortable breaths... and, as you exhale, notice... just notice how comfortable your shoulders can become... that's right, just notice, too, how, when you exhale slowly and deeply, you can just feel that relaxation is beginning to sink in...

[Inducing relaxation.]

I want you to concentrate on your breathing... breathing in pure relaxation and exhaling all the tension in the body... feel yourself relaxing even deeper with each and every breath... and your breathing is so regular... so easy and effortless and you are relaxing more and more... and your entire body is completely and totally relaxing as you drift even deeper down with each and every breath... and you feel a warm, wonderful sense of relaxation and going even deeper down...

[Introducing the staircase as deepening technique.]

Now, as you continue breathing gently, comfortably, and deeply, all I'd like you to do is to picture in your mind... just imagine a beautiful and safe staircase, any kind you like... with ten steps, and you at the top. ... Now, in a moment, I'm going to begin to count from ten to one, and as I count each number I'd like you to take a step down that staircase... see yourself stepping down, feel yourself stepping down, one step for each number I count... and all you need to do is notice, just notice, how much more comfortable and relaxed you can feel at each step, as you go down the staircase... one step for each number that I count... the smaller the number, the farther down the staircase... the farther down the staircase, the more comfortable you can feel... all right, you can begin to get ready... now, I'm going to count... NINE, one step down the staircase... EIGHT, two steps down the staircase... that's fine... SEVEN... three steps down the staircase... and maybe you already notice how much more relaxed you can feel...

I wonder if there are places in your body that feel more relaxed than others... perhaps your shoulders feel more relaxed than your neck... perhaps your legs feel more relaxed than your arms... I don't know, and it really doesn't matter... all that matters is that you feel comfortable... that's all.... SIX... four steps down the staircase... and I wonder if the deep, relaxing, heaviness in your forehead, is already beginning to spread and flow... down, across your eyes, down across your face, into your mouth and jaw... down through your neck. Deep, restful, heavy... FIVE... five steps down the staircase... half of the way down, and already beginning, perhaps, to really enjoy your relaxation and comfort... FOUR... six steps down the staircase... perhaps beginning to notice that the sounds which were distracting become less so... that all the sounds you can hear become a part of your experience of comfort and relaxation... anything you can notice becomes a part of your experience of comfort and relaxation...

THREE... seven steps down the staircase... that's fine... perhaps noticing the heavy, restful, relaxing feeling spreading down into your shoulders, into your arms. ... I wonder if you notice one arm feeling heavier than the other... perhaps your left arm feels a bit heavier than your right... perhaps your right arm feels heavier than your left. ... I don't know, perhaps they both feel equally, comfortably heavy. ... It really doesn't matter... just let yourself become more and more aware of that comfortable heaviness... or is it a feeling of lightness? ... I really don't know, and it really doesn't matter... TWO... eight steps down the staircase... and ONE... nine steps down the staircase, breathing comfortably, slowly, and deeply... noticing that heaviness is really beginning to sink in, as you continue to notice the pleasant, restful, comfortable relaxation just spread through your whole body... and now, TEN steps down the staircase, wondering perhaps what might be happening, perhaps wondering if anything at all is happening... and yet, knowing that it really doesn't matter, feeling so pleasantly restful, just continuing to notice this growing, spreading, comfortable relaxation...

[Utilizing synesthetic suggestions.]

And while you continue to relax, you'll be surprised to find yourself in the middle of a beautiful, secret, enchanted garden. It is the beginning of summer. The air is warm and balmy. The garden stretches for miles and miles. You are walking down a path under a shadowy bower of beautiful flowers. And while enjoying your walk, you might notice at either side of the bower wonderful flower beds with blossoms... and you may wonder how nature may have blended such extraordinary variety of flowers in an endless harmony of colors and perfumes. ... It seems as if any color has its own scent, and any perfume its own color...

[Introducing the magic pool for soothing widespread pain.]

Now, you've come across the long, shadowy bower and just in the middle of this secret garden, there is a delightful swimming pool. I wonder whether you'll like to walk along the edge of the swimming pool, enjoying the peaceful calm of clear, pure waters. You may even wish to take a swim, letting your body float in the waters, drifting way down now... relaxing deeper and deeper. Imagine floating on the water surface, allowing the fresh, magic liquid to penetrate your skin, into your muscles, throughout your body, soothing your pain and regenerating your body.

[Implementing a new, positive self-image and a sense of well-being.]

From now on I want you to have a positive image of your body. Whenever you look at yourself or think of your body image you will do it in a positive manner. Looking at your body in a positive manner will help you to feel good about yourself and to continue to progress toward the body image that you really want. You no longer need to think painful thoughts or to feel painful experiences in your body.

Your body is your temple. It is your sacred private property. You own it and you want the best for it. So from now on I want you to think only positive thoughts and have positive feelings toward your body. You are becoming happy, confident, energetic, and are progressing toward making yourself the best you that you can be. Feel good about yourself, having a good self-image... and continuing to move onward... you are in full control.

And you are really enjoying this incredible experience of well-being, full of energy. I wonder if you'll notice that you'll feel surprised that your experience here today is so much more pleasant and comfortable than you might have expected... that there are no other feelings. ... I wonder if you'll be pleased to notice that today... or any other day... you'll be reminded of how very comfortable you are feeling right now... even more comfortable than you feel even now... comfortable, relaxed... nothing to bother, nothing to disturb. ... I don't know exactly how it will seem... I only know, as perhaps you also know... that your experience will seem surprisingly more pleasant, more comfortable, more restful than you might expect... with nothing to bother, nothing to disturb... whatever you are able to notice... everything can be a part of your experience of comfort, restfulness, and relaxation... nothing really matters but your experience of comfort and relaxation... absolutely deep comfort and relaxation... that's fine.

And now, as you continue to enjoy your comfortable relaxation, I'd like you to notice how very nice it feels to be this way... to really enjoy your own experience, the feelings your whole body can give you... and in a moment, but not yet... not until you're ready...

I'm going to count from one to ten... and as you know, I'd like you to feel yourself going back up the steps... one step for each number... you'll have all the time you need... after all, time is relative... feel yourself slowly and comfortably going back up the steps, one step for each number I count... when I reach eight, your eyes will be almost ready to open... when I reach nine, they will be opened... and, when I reach ten, you'll be fully alert, awake, refreshed... perhaps as though you'd had a nice nap... alert, refreshed, comfortable... and even though you'll still be very comfortable and relaxed, you'll be alert and feeling very well... perhaps surprised, but feeling very well... perhaps ready to be surprised... no hurry, you'll have all the time you need, as you begin to go back up these restful steps...

ONE... TWO... THREE... that's right, feel yourself going back up the steps... ready to be surprised... FOUR... FIVE... halfway back up the stairs... SIX... a quarter of the way back up, more and more alert... no rush, plenty of time... feel yourself becoming more and more alert... SEVEN... that's right... EIGHT... NINE... TEN... that's right... wide awake, alert, relaxed, refreshed... that's fine. How do you feel? Relaxed? Comfortable?

The Space Journey

This second induction procedure focuses upon the following: (1) space-time distortion, (2) dissociation, (3) age regression, (4) eliciting positive expectations and inner resources, and (5) reprogramming a positive future life.

Clinician: And now I want you to take a wonderful space journey...

[Suggesting space-time distortion and dissociation.]

One minute of actual time will seem like 10 minutes to you. Time will go by very, very slowly. It will seem an eternity. ... You are lying in a large, round bed on a platform in a huge, circular, black room. It is the middle of the night and you can admire, through the ceiling, which is a glass transparent dome, the starry sky, the moon, the Milky Way, constellations, and brighter and faraway stars... and while this happens, you sink into a deep sleep and soon you will dream about taking a wonderful journey... and the dream is coming true.

Your bed begins to turn by itself, rising slowly from the platform as if it were driven by mysterious air jets, floating in the air... and the domed ceiling opens like the slices of an orange, letting the magic bed fly over the room, in the moonlight, and in outer space... and while the magic bed flies faster and faster, the earth is farther and farther away, shrinking from view. ... When the magic bed reaches the speed of light, time starts to go backwards: minutes, hours, days, weeks, months, years back... and you become smaller, and smaller, and smaller.

> [Utilizing age regression to recover inner resources of the past to elicit positive expectations and to reprogram a better, future life.]

The time is back, as if a clock or calendar sheets were moved backwards and backwards. ... Now the magic bed has reached its orbit and rotates around the Earth, which appears to your eyes in all its splendor: lands, oceans, clouds, in the alternation of day and night... and this wonderful journey is not only in space but also through time... as the past becomes magically your present time, you can enjoy timeless moments of your past life that have become your present life as happening right now, as if you feel them for the first time with your five senses, your sight, your hearing, your taste and smell, your feelings and emotions.

And all your positive expectations, projects, choices, and resources of that time are still there, ready to be realized and to become the future of your past and the present time of today. So you have a second chance to reprogram your future life by implementing the positive choices that your unconscious mind suggests and avoiding possible errors... that's great!

As you are enjoying this wonderful journey, the magic bed has completed its orbit around the earth and begins its descent, attracted by the earth's gravity... now the speed is decreasing rapidly and time starts to flow again: seconds, minutes, hours, days, months, years... and you gradually regain your present age, while the bed is approaching the earth and the open dome of your room, landing gently on the platform in the center of the bedroom.

And while your dream has come to the end, the night is still deep and you continue sleeping. In a few moments, when you'll be ready, I'll wake you up from your sleep and your trance by counting down from ten to one and you'll wake up relaxed, refreshed, and with happy memories of a wonderful dream.

Conclusion

FMS is a complex, debilitating, functional pain syndrome characterized by chronic, severe, widespread musculoskeletal pain associated with fatigue, nonrestorative sleep, psychopathological concomitants, cognitive/emotional dysfunction, and overall poor HRQoL. Management of FMS may be challenging, as it seems to be refractory to most treatments. However, recent evidence supports the notion that hypnosis, combined with a daily practice of self-hypnosis, may be an effective adjunct tool in addition to standard medical treatment, for pain control and improved HRQoL. Long-term treatment is often needed for positive therapeutic outcome, with pain relief being maintained and even improved across time.

References

Bernardy, K., Füber, N., Klose, P., & Häuser, W. (2011). Efficacy of hypnosis/guided imagery in fibromyalgia syndrome: A systematic review and a meta-analysis of controlled trials. *BMC Musculoskeletal Disorders, 12*, 133.

Bernardy, K., Klose, P., Busch, A. J., Choy, E. H., & Häuser, W. (2013). Cognitive behavioural therapies for fibromyalgia. *Cochrane Database of Systematic Review, 9*, CD009796.

Castel, A., Pérez, M., Sala, J., Padrol, A., & Rull, M. (2007). Effect of hypnotic suggestion on fibromyalgic pain: Comparison between hypnosis and relaxation. *European Journal of Pain, 11*, 463–468.

D'Aoust, R. F., Rossiter, A. G., Elliott, A., Ji, M., Lengacher, C., & Groer, M. (2017). Women veterans, a population at risk of fibromyalgia: The associations between fibromyalgia, symptoms and quality of life. *Military Medicine, 182*, e1828-e1835.

De Benedittis, G. (2001). The revolving doors of pain: Hypnotic synaesthesia for modulation of the pain experience. In: C. Loriedo & B. Peter (Eds.), *The new hypnosis. The utilization of personal resources* (pp. 33–48). Münich, Germany: MEG-Stiftung.

De Benedittis, G. (2012). *Hypnotherapy for fibromyalgia: A long-term controlled study.* Presented at the 14th World Congress on Pain, Milan, Italy.

De Benedittis, G. (2014). *Fibromyalgia and post-traumatic stress disorder: The missing link?* Presented at the 15th World Congress on Pain, Buenos Aires, Argentina.

De Benedittis, G. (2016). Hypnosis and Fibromyalgia. In: G. Elkins (Ed.), *Handbook of medical and psychological hypnosis* (pp. 235-244). New York, NY: Springer.

De Benedittis, G., & Malafronte, M. L. (2014). *Coping with fibromyalgia: What we have learned from hypnosis, a review of the literature and new, innovative hypnotic approaches to widespread, refractory pain.* Presented at the 15th World Congress on Pain, Buenos Aires, Argentina.

Felitti, V. J., Anda, R. F., Nordenberg, D., Williamson, D. F., Spitz, A. M., Edwards, V., ... Marks, J. S. (1998). Relationship of childhood abuse and household dysfunction to many of the leading causes of death in adults: The adverse childhood experiences (ACE) study. *American Journal of Preventative Medicine, 14,* 245-258.

Foa, E. B., Cashman, L., Jaycox, L., & Perry, K. (1997). The validation of a self-report measure of posttraumatic stress disorder: The posttraumatic diagnostic scale. *Psychological Assessment, 9,* 445–451.

Haanen, H. C., Hoenderdos, H. T., van Romunde, L. K., Hop, W. C., Mallee, C., Terwiel, J. P., & Hekster, G. B. (1991). Controlled trial of hypnotherapy in the treatment of refractory fibromyalgia. *Journal of Rheumatology, 18,* 72–75.

Häuser, W., Kosseva, M., Üceyler, N., Klose, P., & Sommer, C. (2011). Emotional, physical, and sexual abuse in fibromyalgia syndrome: A systematic review with meta-analysis. *Arthritis Care & Research, 63,* 808–820.

Häuser, W., Galek, A., Erbslöh-Möller, B., Köllner, V., Kühn-Becker, H., Langhorst, J., Petermann, F., ... Glaesmer, H. (2013). Posttraumatic stress disorder in fibromyalgia syndrome: Prevalence, temporal relationship between posttraumatic stress and fibromyalgia symptoms, and impact on clinical outcome. *Pain, 154,* 1216–1223.

Jensen, M. P. (2016). Pain Management: Chronic Pain. In: G. Elkins (Ed.), *Handbook of medical and psychological hypnosis* (pp. 341-360). New York, NY: Springer.

Jiao, J., Vincent, A., Cha, S. S., Luedtke, C. A., & Oh, T. H. (2015). Association of abuse history with symptom severity and quality of life in patients with fibromyalgia. *Rheumatology International, 35,* 547-553.

Kuchinad, A., Schweinhardt, P., Seminowicz, D. A., Wood, P. B., Chizh, B. A., & Bushnell, M. C. (2007). Accelerated brain gray matter loss in fibromyalgia patients: Premature aging of the brain? *The Journal of Neuroscience, 27,* 4004–4007.

Macfarlane, G.J., Kronisch, C., Dean, L. E., Atzeni, F., Häuser, W., Fluss, B., Choy, E., … Jones, G. T. (2017). EULAR revised recommendations for the management of fibromyalgia. *Annals of the Rheumatic Diseases, 76,* e54.

Martínez-Valero, C., Castel, A., Capafons, A., Sala, J., Espejo, B., & Cardeña, E. (2008). Hypnotic treatment synergizes the psychological treatment of fibromyalgia: A pilot study. *American Journal of Clinical Hypnosis, 50,* 311–321.

Paras, M. L., Murad, M. H., Chen, L. P., Goranson, E. N., Sattler, A. L., Colbenson, K. M., Elamin, M. B., … Zirakzadeh, A. (2009). Sexual abuse and lifetime diagnosis of somatic disorders: A systematic review and meta-analysis. *Journal of the American Medical Association, 302,* 550–561.

Picard, P., Jusseaume, C., Boutet, M., Dualé, C., Mulliez, A., & Aublet-Cuvellier, B. (2013). Hypnosis for management of fibromyalgia. *International Journal of Clinical and Experimental Hypnosis, 61,* 111–123.

Schmidt-Wilcke, T., & Diers, M. (2017). New insight into the pathophysiology and treatment of fibromyalgia. *Biomedicine, 5,* pii: E22.

Talotta, R., Bazzichi, L., Di Franco, M., Casale, R ., Batticciotto, A., Gerardi M. C., & Sarzi-Puttini, P. (2017). One year in review 2017: Fibromyalgia. *Clinical and Experimental Rheumatology. 35 (suppl. 105)*, S6-S12.

Thieme, K., & Gracely, R. H. (2009). Are psychological treatments effective for fibromyalgia pain? *Current Rheumatology Reports, 11*, 443–450.

Varinen, A., Kosunen, E., Mattila, K., Koskela, T., & Sumanen, M. (2017). The relationship between childhood adversities and fibromyalgia in the general population. *Journal of Psychosomatic Research, 99*, 137-141.

Walker, E. A., Keegan, D., Gardner, G., Sullivan, M., Bernstein, D., & Katon, W. J. (1997). Psychosocial factors in fibromyalgia compared with rheumatoid arthritis: Sexual, physical, and emotional abuse and neglect. *Psychosomatic Medicine, 59*, 572–577.

Whibley, D., Dean , L. E., Basu, N. (2016). Management of widespread pain and fibromyalgia. *Current Treatment Options in Rheumatology, 2*, 312-320.

Wolfe, F., Smithe, H. A., Yunus, M. B., Bennett, R. M., Bombardier, C., Goldenberg, D. L., Tugwell, P., ... Sheon, R. P. (1990). The American College of Rheumatology 1990 criteria for the classification of fibromyalgia: Report of the multicentre criteria committee. *Arthritis and Rheumatology, 33*, 160–172.

Wolfe, F., Clauw, D. J., Fitzcharles, M. A., Goldenberg, D. L., Häuser, W., Katz, R. S., Mease, P., ... Walitt, B. (2016). 2016 Revisions to the 2010/2011 fibromyalgia diagnostic criteria. *Seminars in Arthritis and Rheumatism, 46*, 319-329.

Zech, N., Hansen, E., Bernardy, K., & Häuser, W. (2017). Efficacy, acceptability and safety of guided imagery/hypnosis in fibromyalgia: A systematic review and meta-analysis of randomized control trials. *European Journal of Pain, 21*, 217-227.

CHAPTER 5

Hypnotic Treatment of Chronic Gastrointestinal Pain

Olafur S. Palsson

Olafur Palsson is a clinical psychologist and Professor of Medicine in the UNC Center for Functional GI & Motility Disorders at the University of North Carolina at Chapel Hill. His research focuses on irritable bowel syndrome (IBS) and other functional gastrointestinal disorders, including research studies on epidemiology, physiology, psychosocial aspects, diagnostic classifications, and psychological interventions. In 1995, Dr. Palsson developed the first fully scripted hypnosis treatment course for a gastrointestinal disorder. This treatment protocol for IBS has been tested and found efficacious in seven published research studies and has been used for treating the disorder by more than 600 clinicians across the U.S. Dr. Palsson has also collaborated with other investigators on developing and empirically testing hypnosis interventions for other gastrointestinal disorders, including ulcerative colitis, functional abdominal pain, and functional heartburn.

* * *

Gastrointestinal (GI) pain lies at the heart of some of the most common of all human ailments, such as irritable bowel syndrome (IBS), functional dyspepsia, and pediatric functional abdominal pain. In randomized controlled trials, hypnosis interventions have been shown to substantially improve the symptoms of each of these common, pain-centered GI conditions (Palsson, 2015), demonstrating that hypnosis is a powerful tool for addressing pain in the GI tract. In some clinical trials, abdominal pain is reduced by half or more on average, even in patients whose pain has already proven refractory to medical intervention efforts (Gonsalkorale et al., 2002; Palsson et al., 2002).

The reason for this potency of clinical hypnosis for improving GI pain is undoubtedly the very active and dynamic connection between the brain and the gut, which is often referred to as the brain-gut axis (Mayer & Tillisch, 2011; Mayer et al., 2006). In recent years, research has shown that the central nervous system and the digestive tract are far from being independent organ systems. Rather, they communicate continually with each other via a bi-directional information highway consisting of nerves, immune signals, and hormones.

It is now clear that the brain plays an important role in everyday monitoring and regulation of GI activity and exerts frequent guidance and tuning influences in order to adjust the operations of the gut to the shifting requirements of everyday activity. The GI tract sends a continuous stream of messages to the brain with information about its activity and internal events. The brain interprets this gut input and reacts as needed by sending feedback to the GI tract to stimulate adjustments in gut muscle activity, secretion, and immune activity.

The brain generally keeps most of the incoming signals from the gut outside of conscious awareness. However, when those signals are unusually strong—when they are indicative of gut injury, inflammation, or illness, or in situations of heightened perceived threat—the brain may elevate gut sensations to conscious notice and may bring more cognitive and emotional processing to bear on those signals. Under such circumstances, the brain furthermore reduces its normal active dampening (descending inhibition) of nerve signals from the gut coming up the spine, which also contributes to pushing gut sensations above the threshold of conscious awareness. When such heightened brain sensitization to gut sensations and increased cognitive and emotional involvement become long-lasting, this constitutes a brain-gut dysfunction. It is a dysregulation of the normal brain-gut homeostatic control system that is thought to be a key causal mechanism in most chronic, pain-centered GI disorders (Mayer & Tillisch, 2011), such as IBS and functional dyspepsia.

Since cognitive and emotional regions of the brain are intimately involved in causing and maintaining heightened perception of GI sensations, this provides a natural way to intervene with psychological treatment, such as hypnosis, to improve chronic pain problems in the digestive tract (Moser & Peter, 2017).

Hypnotic Treatment Approaches for Chronic GI Pain

There are many ways to address chronic GI pain problems with hypnosis and most of these ways are not specific to GI pain, but rather are techniques used to treat chronic pain in general. In my work with numerous GI patients over the years, and in my efforts to develop and test standardized hypnosis interventions for a number of pain-centered digestive tract disorders, I have settled on a particular hypnotic approach that seems to yield a high rate of success. In a nutshell, this approach consists of (1) taking great care to only deliver therapeutic suggestions under conditions of optimal receptivity, (2) using suggestions that simultaneously target four different aspects of the GI pain problem, and (3) tying suggestions for therapeutic change explicitly to vividly experienced imagery.

In my 25 years of hypnosis work with digestive tract disorders, in clinical practice and in research, this approach has proven valuable for treating a variety of chronic GI problems. It has been applied with high rates of success in my own research studies and by several other investigators for IBS (Barabasz & Barabasz, 2006; Gerson et al., 2013; Lovdahl et al., 2015; Palsson et al., 2002, 2006), abdominal pain in children (van Tilburg et al., 2009), functional heartburn (Riehl et al., 2016), inflammatory bowel disease (Keefer et al., 2013), and globus sensation (Kiebles et al., 2010). I have also used this approach extensively in my clinical practice with a variety of other GI pain conditions such as functional (non-cardiac) chest pain and anorectal pain.

Ensuring an Optimally Receptive State

Helping patients to attain a receptive mental state for hypnotic intervention is the first and most time-consuming part of this particular hypnotic approach. This is not accomplished by simply inducing a hypnotic state. While that might be sufficient for certain highly motivated individuals with good hypnotic ability, it is not enough for the many patients who have more limited hypnotic capacity or who are doubtful of the value of the treatment.

Many patients with chronic pain are quite understandably skeptical, overtly or covertly, about the prospects of something as exotic as hypnosis helping to resolve their health problem, especially when multiple, far more face-valid (at least, face-valid to them) therapies have proven ineffective. Many of these patients will need more preparation in the hypnosis session than a hypnotic induction and ordinary trance deepening in order to make it likely that they will benefit from the intervention. They will still be, even after the induction, in a mental place where they might critically appraise and reject therapeutic suggestions, and anything that is said will likely not fully benefit them unless further steps are taken to remove those obstacles.

After a hypnotic induction, I therefore spend a long time in each session guiding the patients into a low-arousal physical state through autogenic-type suggestions, emphasizing imagining and experiencing heaviness, limpness, and warmth, while encouraging them to allow things to happen automatically and to take a stance of simply observing what is happening in response to their imagination. I then induce dissociation from the here-and-now through vivid imagery of a different place. I describe the imaginary places in great detail, asking the patients to experience them mentally as clearly as they can in multiple senses, and I often transport the patients mentally from one place to another to further augment the dissociation. The overall idea is that a combination of extended, profound, autonomic relaxation; highly activated imagination, adoption of voluntary effortlessness, and controlled dissociation puts a person in a dreamy and accepting mental state, where critical-analytical thinking is optimally suspended.

These are all elements commonly applied in hypnotherapy in general, of course, but the difference here is the extent to which they are used; this part often takes up 80% of the total duration of the hypnosis session. Only after that point, in the last minutes of hypnosis, do I apply therapeutic suggestions; for they can then be assumed to have maximum chance of positive effect, as they are highly unlikely to be countered by doubts, negative feelings, or critical-analytic appraisal in the patients' minds. One advantage of this approach is that the hypnotic suggestions used can be more direct and explicit than might be reasonable if such extensive efforts to induce favorable conditions for uncritical acceptance had not been made. After delivering the therapeutic suggestions at this late point in the session, and linking them to the imagery, I re-alert the patients.

Addressing Four Dimensions of GI Pain

I generally think that it is most effective to simultaneously target four different aspects of GI pain in a hypnosis intervention: (1) the attentional, (2) perceptual, (3) emotional, and (4) physiological dimensions of the problem.

As hypervigilance to sensory input from the GI tract is a major contributor to chronic GI pain conditions, correction of excessive attention to gut sensory input by means of hypnotic suggestions is a key task for achieving pain amelioration. The great power of post-hypnotic suggestions to alter attentional focus involuntarily, in circumscribed ways, for long durations after hypnosis sessions, can be put to highly valuable use here.

Suggesting that the patients forget to pay attention to GI sensations for longer periods, day by day, is a surprisingly simple and effective way to neutralize the hypervigilance that fuels pain experience. I often like to add to this suggestions that instead of attending to pain, the patients find themselves drawn to paying more attention to positive and interesting things in their lives. For example,

In the coming days, starting tomorrow, you will probably be surprised to find that you experience stretches of time where you just completely forget to notice the pain in your esophagus. Over time, from one day to the next, this will

happen more and more often, and the periods of forgetting to notice pain or discomfort will gradually become longer as well. Instead of paying attention to uncomfortable sensations in your esophagus, your attention will instead be pulled irresistibly toward things that you find personally meaningful and interesting in a positive way. This will enable you to enjoy your life more and more without being troubled by pain.

Pain-exacerbating hypervigilance can be further neutralized with suggestions that distinguish ordinary sensations from sensations that might signal something being wrong. Patients are often reluctant to accept the idea of ceasing to pay attention to their pain altogether because of the possibility that the pain might signify something dangerous to their health. By building a provision for noticing pain if it is medically necessary into the hypnotic suggestions, their minds are likely to be more accepting of letting go of most of their painful sensations. For example,

Of course, you would still be able to notice pain in your bowels if your body really needed to warn you about something serious regarding your health, even though your mind is letting go more and more of keeping track of the ordinary sensations inside your intestines that previously might have caused you discomfort.

The perceptual factor in the intervention deals with the intensity and perceived qualities of the pain. One way of addressing this aspect is to simply suggest that the pain becomes milder and less noticeable over time; therefore, this is always a part of my therapeutic approach. However, changing the qualitative nature of the pain can also be very useful. With the assumption that it is easier for the brain to modify its interpretation of the qualities of the pain signals than it is to block perception of them altogether, I often like to suggest that the pain is gradually experienced as morphing into a different sensation.

Usually, I suggest a transition to a warm feeling—or in the case of burning pain like heartburn, to a cool sensation. For example,

Gradually you will probably also notice that something interesting and curious is happening to your pain: More and more, the pain in your stomach feels different than when you experienced it before. Not only will it seem like it is getting milder in the coming days, with steadily fewer bad days and more and more good days over time... but it will most likely also gradually feel more like a different sensation altogether...

It will gradually feel more like a warm sensation to you instead of pain... and warmth is, of course, a much less bothersome sensation than pain.

From one day to the next, you will probably feel this interesting shifting happening in the nature of the sensations in your abdomen... a gradual change from a feeling of pain to a warm feeling instead that does not bother you nearly as much... and might, in fact, not bother you at all.

Chronic GI pain has a substantial affective component, and it is clear from the research literature that GI symptom severity is in many cases amplified by high life stress and negative emotions (Konturek et al., 2011). Targeting this emotional factor with hypnotic suggestions is therefore another practical way to chip away at a GI pain problem. This can be done by directly suggesting immunity of the pain to impact from stressors or negative life events. For example,

Stressful or negative experiences in your daily life that you might have expected to make you feel worse in your bowels before will more and more seem to have no effect on how you feel physically, like your body is protected from, and immune to, those outside influences. No matter what goes on in your life, it somehow does not seem to be able to affect your intestines or cause discomfort or pain there anymore.

Facilitating a general sense of emotional well-being can also neutralize the contributions of negative emotions to pain experience. To this end, I typically help the patients gain a sense of profound emotional comfort in the hypnosis session. This is easy to do, as the deep physical relaxation that is a part of every session typically has already facilitated a comfortable sense of mental tranquility; but I also reinforce that emotional well-being with direct suggestions.

I then use post-hypnotic suggestions to send that feeling of comfort home with the patients. I do this by suggesting that their mind automatically carries the sense of comfort and well-being they are experiencing in the hypnosis session home with them after the session. And, the sense of comfort will stay with them longer and longer after the sessions with each successive visit.

Post-hypnotic suggestions can furthermore be used to isolate the patients' emotions from the sensory part of pain to diminish GI pain experience. This is done by suggesting that the pain does not seem to "get to them" in the same way as it did previously. For example,

From now on you will notice more and more, that even if you experience pain in your abdomen, it somehow does not bother you as much as before, and it is not able to get to you emotionally in the same way as before...

Instead, you will experience the pain almost as if you are observing something from a distance and that it does not matter that much to you.

Finally, addressing the physiological component of GI pain means targeting physiological processes that are likely to contribute to causing the pain. Pain in the GI tract is often triggered or amplified by some internal events, such as contractile activity or inflammation, even though brain sensitization is viewed as being primarily responsible for the severity of the problem.

To the degree that likely physiological contributing factors can be identified or assumed, the hypnotherapeutic approach should take those into account. Pain should, for example, not be addressed in isolation if it is a part of a syndrome, such as in IBS where stool consistency abnormalities and smooth muscle hyper-reactivity collude with central nervous system pain sensitization to produce the pain that is the cardinal symptom. Facilitating normal and regular bowel functioning through hypnotic suggestions and imagery can calm the disturbed intestinal activity that triggers pain episodes.

Similarly, in functional dyspepsia, inadequate accommodation of the stomach wall to filling of the stomach during eating or drinking often plays a role in producing discomfort or pain. That physiological contributor should be addressed in hypnosis, in addition to targeting the pain and discomfort directly. For example,

You will probably be pleased, and perhaps a bit surprised, to notice—starting with your next meal—that your stomach feels much more comfortable than before, whenever you eat or drink. You will feel more comfortable from one day to the next.

From now on, your stomach relaxes quickly and easily as soon as you take the first bite of every meal or the first sip of every drink so that it can comfortably accept the food and drink it receives.

I believe that all four of these different aspects of GI pain—attentional, perceptual, emotional, and physiological—should preferably be addressed with hypnotic and post-hypnotic suggestions in every treatment session, in varying combinations and with plenty of repetition and qualifiers that make the suggestions hard to logically reject (such as "probably," "likely," and "I would not be surprised if").

Tying Suggestions to Imagery

It has been my observation over the years that hypnotic suggestions seem to become more potent if they are tied explicitly to vividly experience mental imagery that illustrates the desired therapeutic effect directly or metaphorically. For pain in the digestive tract, where the gut is likely to be hypersensitive to intra-luminal stimuli such as certain foods, a typical imagery I use is the visualized application of strong protective coating to the inside of the bowels, which shields the bowel wall from all irritation and uncomfortable stimuli. For functional heartburn, I sometimes ask the patients to imagine swallowing a bright and radiant neon blue (i.e., easy to visualize) drink. I then ask them to imagine the drink going down through the esophagus producing a powerful, soothing and numbing effect that lingers after the hypnosis session and grows stronger over time.

I also tie therapeutic GI sensations to the experiences of the imagined locations where I bring subjects (these are sometimes chosen partly for that purpose). For example, the rhythmic sound of small waves lapping against the shore when relaxing on an imagined beach can be used as a metaphor for ordinary GI sensations. These sensations do not need to bother the patients and signify nothing threatening. In an effort to ensure the best results from use of imagery, I use several different types of detailed imagery across the treatment course, as some may resonate more with individual patients than others.

Sample Script of Therapeutic Intervention for Abdominal Pain

The script below is an example of a typical intervention part of a hypnosis session for GI pain. It contains examples of suggestions that address all the four aspects of such problems described above and also illustrates how I tie therapeutic suggestions to imagery.

[This therapeutic intervention is delivered after a hypnotic induction, extensive physical relaxation and trance deepening, and after the patient has been mentally transported into an imagined scene described in detail—lying on her back on a blanket on a grassy bank by the side of a beautiful pond in a forest clearing, on a bright and sunny day.]

Just continue to enjoy lying there comfortably on the blanket, relaxing your whole body... letting your entire body—every muscle from head to toe—relax... relax completely...

Relaxing like that, totally at ease, far out in nature on this beautiful day. ... You are so very far away from anybody and anything that could bother you that it seems hard to even think about your everyday cares...

None of it matters right now... simply allow yourself to enjoy the profound sense of calm and the beauty of nature around you. Not a care or concern in the whole world. ... Nothing matters now except enjoying this deep feeling of well-being and relaxation that fills your mind and body.

And you are probably feeling so far away from all discomfort, that you might also feel inside your body like nothing can bother you there. You probably feel inside like nothing can disturb your deep comfort, like nothing at all can upset you inside your body or cause you discomfort or pain.

And if you pay close attention as you lie there and relax and let your body soak up this healthy feeling of comfort, you can probably feel the comfortable warmth from the sun as it shines on the front of your shirt... warming up your belly through your clothes. Notice this now... notice whether you can feel that warm sensation on the surface of your abdomen...

Whatever you can feel is fine... if you cannot feel it very clearly you then can at least picture it... the bright warming sun shining on your shirt. But you can probably feel it in your body now, if you concentrate... and if you can, then focus on that sensation of warmth.

It is a pleasant feeling... a very pleasant sensation... and it is growing stronger... Your abdomen is feeling warmer... and warmer and warmer... And you can let that delightful warm feeling spread from the surface of your abdomen and allow it to flow deep into your stomach so that it fills you with a sense of comfort inside your abdomen... just by thinking about it you can let that warm and soothing sensation go deep inside you and fill your abdomen... filling you inside with a delightful soothing and healthy sense of warmth and comfort... healthy warmth and comfort inside... making your entire abdominal area feel good... making you feel so very comfortable inside your abdomen.

After you wake up from this state in a little while, you will continue to carry that deep sense of healthy comfort with you inside your body. And it will remain with you for days, making you feel healthier inside, in your stomach and intestines, as you go about your everyday business.

And in the next few days, you will probably start to notice more and more that things have really changed in a positive and healthy way in your abdomen. Experiences that you might have expected to cause you discomfort in your stomach or intestines before do not bother you any longer.

No matter what goes on in your life, your stomach and your intestines seem to remain unaffected; like they are immune to all stress and disturbance in your life... just like nothing can bother you or cause you discomfort when you are enjoying relaxing out there in nature... miles and miles away from all your cares and concerns.

You will probably find also that even when you do notice some sensations in your abdomen, those sensations are different in nature from now on... where you might have expected before to feel discomfort in your abdomen, it will from now on feel more and more like a different and more pleasant sensation... perhaps even like the kind of pleasant warm feeling in your stomach and intestines that you are probably experiencing right now.

Of course, you would still be able to feel pain or discomfort inside your stomach or intestines if your body really needed to warn you about something serious regarding your health. But everyday discomfort in your belly will be disappearing from your life more and more in the coming days and weeks, or the discomfort may be turning into some more pleasant and far less bothersome sensations.

Your intestines will also increasingly function with a healthy and comfortable and quiet natural rhythm that is barely noticeable and causes you no discomfort and no pain. No discomfort and no pain... As the sensations in your bowels and stomach become less and less noticeable day by day, you will probably be interested to find that it seems harder to even remember to pay attention to what is going on inside your intestinal tract; instead, it will be easier every day to just forget about it.

This means that longer and longer periods of time will pass without you even paying any attention to the sensations inside you... and that will free your mind up to focus instead on the enjoyable experiences of your everyday life.

And if you happen to feel discomfort in your stomach or in your intestines, you will most likely notice that the discomfort is much milder than before, because your sensitivity to discomfort in your abdomen is steadily fading away more and more, leaving you more comfortable and healthy from one day to the next... more comfortable and healthy in your stomach and intestines day by day, from this day forward.

[This is followed by re-alerting the patient.]

References

Barabasz, A., & Barabasz, M. (2006). Effects of tailored and manualized hypnotic inductions for complicated irritable bowel syndrome patients. *International Journal of Clinical and Experimental Hypnosis, 54*, 100-112.

Gerson, C. D., Gerson, J., & Gerson, M. J. (2013). Group hypnotherapy for irritable bowel syndrome with long-term follow-up. *International Journal of Clinical and Experimental Hypnosis, 61*, 38-54.

Gonsalkorale, W. M., Houghton, L. A., & Whorwell, P. J. (2002). Hypnotherapy in irritable bowel syndrome: A large-scale audit of a clinical service with examination of factors influencing responsiveness. *American Journal of Gastroenterology, 97*, 954-961.

Keefer, L., Taft, T. H., Kiebles, J. L., Martinovich, Z., Barrett, T. A., & Palsson, O. S. (2013). Gut-directed hypnotherapy significantly augments clinical remission in quiescent ulcerative colitis. *Alimentary Pharmacolology & Therapeutics, 38*, 761-771.

Kiebles, J. L., Kwiatek, M. A., Pandolfino, J. E., Kahrilas, P. J., & Keefer, L. (2010). Do patients with globus sensation respond to hypnotically assisted relaxation therapy? A case series report. *Diseases of the Esophagus, 23*, 545-553.

Konturek, P. C., Brzozowski, T., & Konturek, S. J. (2011). Stress and the gut: Pathophysiology, clinical consequences, diagnostic approach and treatment options. *Journal of Physiology and Pharmacology, 62*, 591-599.

Lovdahl, J., Ringstrom, G., Agerforz, P., Tornblom, H., & Simren, M. (2015). Nurse-administered, gut-directed hypnotherapy in IBS: Efficacy and factors predicting a positive response. *American Journal of Clinical Hypnosis, 58*, 100-114.

Mayer, E. A., & Tillisch, K. (2011). The brain-gut axis in abdominal pain syndromes. *Annual Review of Medicine, 62,* 381-396.

Mayer, E. A., Tillisch, K., & Bradesi, S. (2006). Review article: Modulation of the brain-gut axis as a therapeutic approach in gastrointestinal disease. *Alimentary Pharmacology & Therapeutics, 24,* 919-933.

Moser, G., & Peter, J. (2017). [Brain-gut axis and gut-directed hypnosis - success of an integrated psychosomatic treatment in gastroenterology]. *Zeitschrift Fur Psychosomatiche Mediczin Und Psychotherapie, 63,* 5-19.

Palsson, O. S. (2015). Hypnosis treatment of gastrointestinal disorders: A comprehensive review of the empirical evidence. *American Journal of Clinical Hypnosis, 58,* 134-158.

Palsson, O. S., Turner, M. J., Johnson, D. A., Burnett, C. K., & Whitehead, W. E. (2002). Hypnosis treatment for severe irritable bowel syndrome: Investigation of mechanism and effects on symptoms. *Digestive Diseases and Sciences, 47,* 2605-2614.

Palsson, O. S., Turner, M. J., & Whitehead, W. E. (2006). Hypnosis home treatment for irritable bowel syndrome: A pilot study. *International Journal of Clinical and Experimental Hypnosis, 54,* 85-99.

Riehl, M. E., Pandolfino, J. E., Palsson, O. S., & Keefer, L. (2016). Feasibility and acceptability of esophageal-directed hypnotherapy for functional heartburn. *Diseases of the Esophagus, 29,* 490-496.

van Tilburg, M. A., Chitkara, D. K., Palsson, O. S., Turner, M., Blois-Martin, N., Ulshen, M., & Whitehead, W. E. (2009). Audio-recorded guided imagery treatment reduces functional abdominal pain in children: A pilot study. *Pediatrics, 124,* e890-897.

CHAPTER 6

Hypnosis in the Management of Chronic Regional Pain Syndrome

Stella C. Nkenke

Stella C. Nkenke is a physician in private practice in both Germany and Austria. While she incorporates hypnosis in virtually all aspects of her practice, her particular field of expertise is facilitating weight loss through hypnosis and optimal nutrition, with a special emphasis on micronutrients. An additional facet of Dr. Nkenke's medical hypnosis practice is the management of pain. She helps to prepare women for childbirth, and she assists patients with complex regional pain syndrome (CRPS) to effectively cope with their symptoms. Dr. Nkenke has a history of CRPS herself and has discovered that hypnosis and self-hypnosis are powerful tools for overcoming the symptoms of this illness. Her aim is to establish medical hypnosis as a key component in the treatment of CRPS, especially in those patients who are not satisfied with standard medical care. It is well known that conventional biomedical CRPS treatment has clear limitations. Dr. Nkenke believes that supporting a patient in developing acceptance of his or her disease is as important for the effective management of CRPS as all other treatment approaches offered by today's medicine.

* * *

When patients come into my clinic with complex regional pain syndrome (CRPS), they often start by telling me, "I don't know what to do anymore! It burns like fire! You cannot imagine the feeling, it's so terribly painful. I've already tried everything the doctors at the clinic recommended!"

As a former CRPS patient myself, I remember exactly how it burns; and as a doctor I also know that there are effective treatment options that unfortunately are rarely used. Although hypnotherapy is not yet a standard method for dealing with CRPS, it is hopefully only a matter of time before studies confirm its efficacy for the treatment of CRPS. For patients, hypnosis is often their "last hope;" but I think it should also be one of the first treatment options.

Treatment recommendations for CRPS are usually based on medication management together with some combination of occupational and/or physiotherapy. Psychotherapy is mentioned in treatment guidelines, but only for patients who do not respond to standard treatment or for patients with a psychological comorbidity. In my experience, and regardless of the severity of the episode, patients with CRPS can benefit from hypnotherapy in many different ways, and hypnotherapists treating CRPS could benefit from a deeper knowledge of this disease.

What is CRPS?

Complex regional pain syndrome, formerly known as reflex sympathetic dystrophy or Sudeck's disease, is an unusual, debilitating syndrome that can develop in 2%-5% of patients after a variety of minor or moderately serious tissue injuries (Sandroni et al., 2003). CRPS usually occurs after an injury such as a wrist fracture; however, it can also develop after minor injuries such as sprains, pinpricks, scratches, or immobilizations (Breier, 2008; Marinus et al., 2010). In some cases, CRPS appears to develop spontaneously.

Women are typically affected more often than men, adults more than children, and CRPS occurs more often in the upper extremities than in the lower ones (Gierthmüller & Baron, 2010). It occurs most frequently in patients who are between 40 and 70 years old, although younger and older individuals can have the condition as well (Veldmann et al., 1993; Sandroni et al., 2003).

CRPS is characterized by disproportional chronic pain intensity, significant stiffness, involvement of the autonomous nervous system, and sensory motor symptoms (Marinus et al., 2010). The nature and location of the pain is not related to the triggering event and is not limited to the innervation area of peripheral nerves (Gierthmüller & Baron, 2010).

Recent neurophysiological studies have been consistent in finding that central mechanisms rather than peripheral ones play an essential role. The appearance of a prolonged reaction of the sympathetic nervous system at the site of the injured area is physiological; however, it is the persistence and over-excitation that are pathological. Patients have an abnormal cortical body map of the affected limb and its movement (Jänig & Baron, 2003; Barber & Moreni, 2015).

Clinical Presentation and Diagnostic Criteria

Table 1 lists and describes the symptoms associated with CRPS. In the acute phase, the injured limb is usually extremely painful, red, warm, and swollen. Initially, the symptoms of CRPS are non-specific; however, they usually change over time and often vary from person to person (Marinus et al., 2010). The diagnosis is primarily based on clinical considerations and exclusions. For some patients, the symptoms disappear on their own. For others, the symptoms can persist for months or years and contribute to a significant reduction in quality of life (Veldman et al., 1993). As the disorder persists, pain does not subside but often spreads and can even emerge on the opposite or ipsilateral limb.

Table 6-1. Complex Regional Pain Syndrome symptoms, by category.

Symptom or Condition	Description	Presentation
Somatosensory disorders of the affected limb or area		
Burning pain	Often intensified by movement, active or passive	
Allodynia	Normal contact of the skin is experienced as very painful	The sleeve of a sweater can be intolerable
Hyperalgesia	Painful Stimuli evoke more intense pain than usual	
Thermal hyperalgesia	Sensitive to cold or heat	Sun shining on a limb can cause sudden pain
Autonomous sympathetic disorders		
Edema	Initially often warm and soft but can also become hard and fibrotic	
Changes in skin temperature sometimes reduced	The affected limb may feel warmer or cooler compared to that of the opposite limb	
Changes in skin color	Can range from white and mottled to red or blue	This can change rapidly, sometimes due to emotional stress
Changes in sweating	Often increased	One limb is sweaty and the other one is normal
Trophic disorders		
Glossy skin	May appear shiny and thin	
Changes in hair/nail growth	Dark hair grows where there was previously none	
Motor disorders		
Restriction of mobility	Passive and active, due to joint stiffness	Stiffness of fingers and wrist
Muscle weakness	Possibly due to diminished activity of the central motor neurons	
Tremor, dystonia, disturbed body perception	Affected limb is perceived as not belonging to the body	Patient needs visual checks to locate arm

Due to its heterogeneity and the fact that it is relatively unknown, CRPS is often overlooked. For example, I know of a 46-year-old man who accidentally stabbed himself in the hand with a pointed tool. He subsequently had surgery at a large hand-surgery clinic for suspected phlegmon. As the pain and swelling continued (i.e., signs of CRPS), his hand was operated on an additional *three more times* in the following week. The initial suspicion of a phlegmon was not confirmed. Unfortunately, after the four surgeries, the pain could not be controlled, even with powerful analgesics. Finally, a neurologist was asked to see the patient and made the diagnosis of CRPS.

What Treatments are Most Effective?

The therapy for patients with CRPS continues to be challenging for both the practitioner and the patient. To minimize the chances of negative, long-term outcomes, early interdisciplinary pain management involving occupational therapy, physiotherapy, psychotherapy, and pain therapy should be the primary goal (Bialas, 2013). A high level of active participation is required; patience and discipline are also necessary.

Patients must daily, consistently, and independently, continue therapy on their own. One common treatment is mirror therapy, an approach originally developed for the relief of phantom limb pain. A mirror box is used (a box with two mirrors in the center—one facing the other) with the goal of recreating the illusion of painless and free movement in the affected limb. This allows the patient's brain to "reconnect" with their affected limb, thereby freeing the patient from pain and functional disability (Lebon et al., 2017).

Medications, if needed, should be symptom and diagnosis oriented. Bisphosphonates can be used for osteoporotic changes, and glucocorticoids for overheating and edema. Anticonvulsants and antidepressants are used to treat neuropathic pain and can sometimes benefit patients with CRPS.

There are also a number of invasive therapeutic procedures such as ketamine infusions, sympathetic nerve blocks, spinal cord-related electrical stimulation, and intrathecal administration of baclofen that are sometimes offered when conservative treatment options have been exhausted (Bialas, 2013). The efficacy of these treatments is highly variable and none have been shown to quickly and effectively cure CRPS (Bussa et al., 2015).

Psychological treatment has been found useful as a component of a multidisciplinary approach to fostering a reduction in pain intensity (Castelnuovo et al., 2016), although it is generally only offered when standard treatment is not successful. Hypnosis, in particular, is offered even more rarely but can be very helpful, as it interacts with the patient's various problems; including, but not limited to, the pain.

Hypnotic suggestion therapy allows a virtual activation of a pathological limb, stimulating the same brain areas activated during true limb mobilization (Lebon et al., 2017). Hypnosis—and especially self-hypnosis—can effectively complement and enrich standard medical therapy. Hypnotic suggestions to encourage patients to experience physical movements stimulate central motor neurons and can accelerate rehabilitation, providing significant benefits to patients with CRPS (Nkenke, 2012).

What Happens if CRPS is not Diagnosed or Treated in Time?

Failure to diagnose or treat CRPS in a timely way may result in a vicious cycle of distressing symptoms leading to chronic pain and limb dysfunction (see Figure 1).

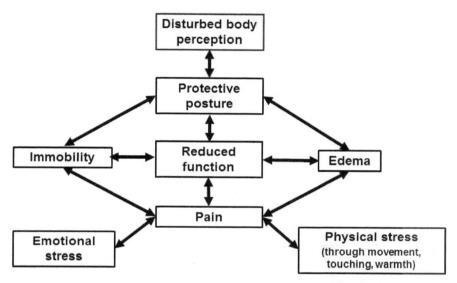

Figure 6-1. The vicious cycle of CRPS-related distressing symptoms leading to chronic pain and limb dysfunction.

With CRPS, the affected limb is often no longer perceived as belonging to the body and the limb is often held in a protective posture. In turn, this guarding restricts movement in the limb and consequently reduces lymphatic drainage, thus promoting edema. Pain is not only caused by the swelling associated with edema, but can also be triggered by other factors. The slightest touch, or even concern about the progression of the disease and ensuing fear of an impending functional loss of an arm or a leg, may spontaneously lead to severe pain. The less the limb is moved, the more the fibrosis and ankylosis of the affected area progress, which is then followed by atrophy and muscle contracture.

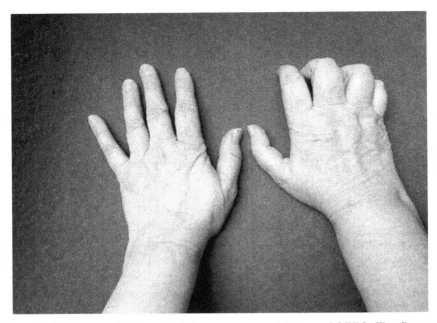

Figure 6-2. 58-year-old patient with a seven-year history of CRPS. The fingers of the right hand cannot be straightened due to stiffness and the muscles are very clearly atrophied in the palm of the right hand.

How can Hypnosis and Hypnotic Suggestion Help?

Before you can work effectively with hypnosis in the treatment of CRPS, there are some important prerequisites to consider:

- Knowledge of the illness
- Good communication
- Therapeutic bonding
- Goal orientation

Many patients with CRPS receive inappropriate messages from clinicians, both verbally and nonverbally. Verbal messages might include:

- "There is no cure and if it spreads out over your body, you will end up in a wheelchair."

- "This hand cannot be healed."

- "Your physiotherapist should not do any painful exercises with you because that prevents healing."

These messages can contribute to poor therapeutic outcomes, especially if the patient believes them. As a clinician, it is important to communicate without providing such negative suggestions (Nkenke, 2012).

On the other hand, therapeutic bonding has a major beneficial effect on the success of the therapy. The extent or severity of the patient's pain is often questioned by clinicians, perhaps because of a lack of knowledge about CRPS, or perhaps because so little is known about this condition in general. CRPS patients are often assumed to have a secondary gain from the condition or an "unstable" personality. They are sometime viewed negatively, which interferes with the outcome. They also sometimes feel like they have to fight to be believed and to be taken seriously by doctors, by their health insurance company, their friends and colleagues, and their family. These are certainly not the best conditions for the healing process. One patient told me, "They don't believe you, that's the worst thing about this disease."

With regard to goal orientation, one comment I often hear is, "I do not need to go back to normal, but back to life." To help a patient effectively define his or her treatment goal, it is useful to divide it into smaller steps. It is necessary to ask questions such as, "What do you want to be able to do next?" and "What do you want to be able to do at the end of the therapy?"

At the beginning of treatment, it can be very useful to regain and be able to start to carry out even simple activities of daily life that were not possible at the beginning of treatment; activities such as holding a knife and a fork, opening a bottle, or developing enough strength and flexibility to grasp a steering wheel and drive again. As treatment continues, and with initial treatment success, the goals can expand; to be able to return to work, play the piano, etc.

Hypnotic Work with CRPS

Although there are many hypnotic approaches that can be used to deal with chronic pain in general, and CRPS in particular, I generally work with CRPS patients using the following approach:

Comfortable Place

Creating an image of a comfortable place is gladly accepted by many patients with CRPS. When they are in their comfortable place, they can relax and focus their thoughts on other things; some may even forget the painful body part for a time, while others may consciously focus on their affected limb to change the pain level.

Some typical comfortable places, such as on a beach in the sun, are not useful for some patients as kinesthetic elements, because the hot sun, hot sand, or cool water are more likely to trigger severe pain. If this is the case, the patient can be encouraged to imagine a completely new situation, perhaps the gentle immersion of the aching limb in healing water or in a morphine bath.

Even memories of real situations, in which the patient felt no pain (despite CRPS), can be helpful. For example, the memory of a pain-free time during an infusion or a sympathetic nerve block. Here, of course, new details can be supplemented. The memory of an infusion might not only provide pain relief but can also "infuse" the patient with a pleasant sense of relaxation or other desirable physical sensations and experiences.

Age Regression (Work with Real Memories) and Age Progression (Experiencing Goal Attainment)

Frequently, patients can no longer imagine performing simple movements, like shaking hands or carrying a shopping bag, with the affected limb. Everything is automatically done using the healthy hand. Patients also report that even in their dreams, they hold their painful body part in a protective posture and do not integrate that body part into movement sequences. Therefore, it is important to reactivate and integrate simple movement patterns in trances. The easiest way to do this is to put patients in a trance by regressing to a time long before the trauma happened; a time when it was natural to move all limbs easily and painlessly. Here is a description of age regression by a patient who frequently practiced this in self-hypnosis:

> "I immerse myself in early experiences; I am able to move freely again and I am pain-free. So I start to imagine early scenes from my childhood, very simple situations like going to school, with the schoolbag on my back, arms swinging happily. As a next step, I allow myself to be "older." Because I was an intensely competitive athlete between the ages of 14 and 20, I simply go into well-known training situations, which I have experienced painlessly a thousand times. So I work in small steps, always getting closer to the current situation. The best part is when I am able to reach my real age within a trance and to move freely in the here and now."

If the experience of moving freely is already possible in trance, then work with age progression can be initiated. It makes sense and is helpful to work and imagine the successful achievement of the patient's goals at the beginning of therapy in order for the future to be experienced as more positive and hopeful.

Trance Exercise for Integration of the Extremity

Since the perceived alienation of the painful body part is most obvious during the day, the following exercise is particularly suitable to practice early in the day. The patient is instructed to imagine any shape that encloses their body and into which something is being filled, whereby the affected extremity is filled last. At this point, patients almost always report that "... it's not flowing in properly, there's a blockage," or something similar. I then let the patient describe what the barrier is like and what it would take to dissolve or remove it, offering them all the real and unreal possibilities available in trance. As soon as it is possible to fill the limb (or whatever body part is painful), the feeling of belonging often returns in the affected limb and the patient feels whole. Many patients report that this is the most important exercise for them as it improves their intuitive willingness to use the limb naturally and to stop guarding.

CReate (your) Personal Solution: Transforming Negative Emotions into Positive Emotions

Because this disease shows very different characteristics and courses, an individual approach tailored to each patient is necessary. The name CRPS triggers negative thoughts in patients and so to combine it with a goal-oriented suggestion, I propose to the patient that the abbreviation CRPS now stands for something completely different and can also mean something quite different; that is, CReate (your) Personal Solution.

Self-Hypnosis

It is imperative that hypnotic strategies be applied daily in self-hypnosis. This may possibly be responsible for the structural changes which have been identified in the brain with successful treatment. Self-hypnosis not only increases the healing perspective but also promotes self-efficacy in the patient. The advantage of self-hypnosis over other therapies is that it can be used almost anywhere and at (almost) any time.

In hypnosis, all possible movement patterns can be played out. A variety of interesting experiences can be generated (in mirror therapy, movements are very one-sided and an apparatus is required). In addition, patients do not experience annoying side effects with hypnosis, as they often do with drug therapy. On the contrary, patients often report positive side-effects; for example, that they can tolerate their otherwise uncomfortable physiotherapy better, that they sleep better (even when these issues are not the direct target of hypnotic suggestions) or, as this patient reports:

> "Since I've been doing my self-hypnosis exercises regularly, I don't need painkillers anymore—I'm very proud of myself. Luckily, no one can read my mind because at work (when my hand suddenly burns), I immediately give my hand a suggestion. Everybody would think I'm crazy but I don't care, because it helps. I would never have thought of that before."

Suggestions for Healing

Patients often perceive any pain or burning sensation as an uncontrollable event signaling deterioration. It is important to get rid of these catastrophic thoughts that are a reliable "predictor of pain" (Jensen, 2015). This is achieved through small, built-in suggestions or by promoting "posthypnotic suggestions" such as, "whenever my hand suddenly sweats or burns, the more rapidly my healing can progress."

Hypnotic strategies in CRPS can intervene not only with pain but at many points of the vicious cycle (see Figure 3, the arrows indicate where hypnosis can intervene); therefore, I consider hypnosis to be particularly useful in the treatment of CRPS.

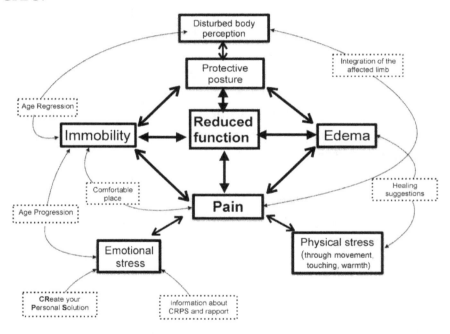

Figure 6-3. Places in the CRPS vicious cycle where hypnotic strategies can effectively intervene.

Example of a Therapeutic Session

Directly before I hypnotize CRPS patients, we find a position—sitting or lying—where the affected limb or other painful area can feel "as safe and comfortable as possible."

The patient must know that they are allowed to change their position any time they wish.

I never use arm levitation in these patients because the goal is to make them feel that everything is integrated, associated. Moreover, I do not want to suggest any changes in the comfortable and safe position the patient has chosen for the process.

Trance Exercise for Better Integration of the Affected Limb

Clinician: And now that you have found a comfortable position in the armchair, please look around... maybe you notice a picture, a chair, or something else... and now if you could close your eyes... you may still see this as an inner image...

[Directs the focus on visual cue, from external to internal.]

and allow yourself to breathe deeply and calmly... and let the air flow out slowly and calmly.

[It is often easier for the patient if the therapist inhales and exhales audibly at the same time, adjusted to the patient's own breathing rhythm.]

Your pace is just right... take your time to set everything up... so it's just right for now, knowing that you can always change and adjust anything that makes it even more comfortable for you... and become aware of it again and enjoy the idea that you do not have to do anything from now on, really nothing, not even listening to my voice... and there are few moments in life when you are supposed to do nothing... so maybe this is a good moment to enjoy doing nothing... and you can let your thoughts come and go just like your breath... in and out... everything is allowed... taking the time you need now.

*[Patients often have the idea that they have to do something
in order for the trance to work. Giving them permission to do
nothing is often helpful.]*

While your conscious mind continues to help with the slow
and comfortable breathing, your unconscious mind can
allow itself to follow other directions or any inner visions. ...
It may feel interesting, when I invite you to imagine that
something envelops your body, like a shell, something that
starts from the bottom and reaches all the way up... maybe a
shell made out of wax or other material, such as plaster,
bronze, or even a cake pan. ... I do not know... and while
you breathe deeply and calmly again... and then slowly
exhale, just take a look at what it will be that surrounds you,
all by itself... and I do not know what material would be
most pleasant for you... and it does not matter if it's soft and
flexible like silicone, or rather sturdy and strong like
metal... take your time and look... just look at it, everything
happens on its own...

*[Patient reports for example that the imagined shell looks like
a cake pan.]*

And now you allow yourself to fill that cake pan... and I do
not know what that looks like and how well you can fill up
your pan, maybe starting from the top... into the right foot
first... or somewhere completely different...

*[Patient reports that a brown mass like chocolate dough, with
a very pleasant temperature, slowly fills the "cake pan" from
below.]*

And just watch how it fills up all by itself, into the calves,
thighs... and I do not know if the right one fills up first, and
then the left one, or if it's already beginning to fill the left
one even though the right side is not full yet... and pay

attention to how it feels, when it begins to fill the abdomen and how everything is completely connected... and everything is one. It slowly fills the chest and everything is one again... it all belongs together, a feeling your body has known for so long, and even if it feels different, it's all okay because it is all one.

> [Emphasize that the feeling of wholeness is known to the body—that the body is one and that no matter how it feels now it is right.]

Then the dough may begin to flow into the left arm, down to the fingertips... slowly, and all you need to do is nothing, just watch... and then the dough would like to flow into the right arm as well, very slowly, softly, and gently, because the right arm is sometimes not allowed to join in, and the dough would like to be allowed to flow in, and you can see how things are already moving on...

> [Patient reports that at the level of the shoulder, there are some things like dark threads that are sewn together, blocking the entrance to the arm, so the dough cannot flow into the arm. The patient imagines that the threads have just been overlooked, and that one just has to remove them, which she then succeeds in doing.]

Watch to see if something else has to be cleared out somewhere or if the dough can now slowly flow into this arm... down to the forearm and the wrist and the fingertips... everything should be filled out and together... this filled pan, which envelops everything and holds everything together securely, so that everything is evenly filled out and whole, the right foot with the left arm, everything is enveloped and connected, the left foot with the right arm, in a completely new, but also familiar old way.

And maybe it takes some more time, like baking, where sometimes the dough has to rest before the next step comes. Maybe you need a bit of rest and time... or you may slowly remove the pan, and feel how everything is already connected, how nice to feel that your arm can now participate more in its own way, as much as it already wants to... feel that good sensation.

And from now on you know that once a day you may slip easily into the baking pan... right in the morning, let the dough pour in gently and then experience that good feeling again... and whenever you feel like the arm is still not part of it, then without having to worry about it, your dough will fill up the shape again and you will get the same feeling as now.

[This gives the patient posthypnotic suggestions; more control over movement of the painful limb or area.]

And once you have inhaled and exhaled three times... now... slowly and in your own rhythm... you can take any time you need in the next two minutes, to stretch slowly and breathe and when you are ready to open your eyes again... maybe you can see the picture, the chair or whatever you saw... before closing your eyes... that will mean to you to take that feeling with you... wherever you go... today.

[Connecting the patient's good feeling with a visual cue.]

Connecting the Label "CRPS" with Positive Emotions and Goals

The clinician asks the patient, "What do you normally associate with CRPS?" The clinician goes on to explain,

Perhaps you attribute some negative feelings towards these four letters, like some other patients who have this diagnosis do. Maybe you focus a lot on your concern about how things will go in the future, or on the anger you feel, maybe because no one can really imagine how crazy this disease is because it not only affects the [body part affected] but the whole person and your life. Or you associate physical reactions, such as an unpleasant burning or tingling in your [body part affected], even when only talking about CRPS. And would it not be nice if those four letters, which have suddenly taken over your daily thoughts and actions, even though you knew nothing about them until recently, could mean something completely different for you from now on? How about if it meant the beginning of a new, individual, and personal way for you to achieve your goals?

CReate your Personal Solution!

Maybe you prefer to close your eyes... because important things are sometimes invisible.

[A brief hypnotic induction could follow here.]

And how would that be for you, if you are allowed to create your own personal solution? You are the expert on yourself and who, besides you, knows what you really need? The letters CRPS will always remind you... any time you hear them... that you can *create your personal solution* because you are special. ... From now on CRPS will sound different to you... and things will be better for you, because you know there is a solution... because you are more than only an affected limb.... From now on CRPS will mean to you that you can find your own way... nothing more and nothing less... you don't need to know now what could be your exact solution... take another breath... and take your time... as much as you need... wait and see what will be helpful... and always, when you are in a situation in which you do not immediately know how to go on... think of, *"create your personal solution"* and go on... because only you are the expert on yourself.

Although hypnotherapy in the treatment of CRPS may sometimes start as the patient's "last hope," I am confident that it holds a key to a new, pain-free, and optimistic future.

References

Barber, A., & Moreni, A. (2015). Place de l'hypnose dans le traitement du SDRC. *Kinésithérapie, la Revue, 15,* 45-49.

Breier, S. (2008). Komplexes regionales Schmerzsyndrom. In B. Waldner-Nilsson, H. Troeger, & A. R. Eigenheer (Eds.), *Handrehabilitation I: Für Ergo-und Physiotherapeuten, Band 1: Grundlagen, Erkrankungen* (339-381). Heidelberg, Germany: Springer.

Bialas, P. (2013). Die Diagnose komplexes regionales Schmerzsyndrom. *Angewandte Schmerztherapie und Palliativmedizin, 6,* 28-33.

Bussa, M., Guttilla, D., Lucia, M., Mascaro, A., & Rinaldi, S., (2015). Complex regional pain syndrome type 1: A comprehensive review. *Acta Anaesthesiologica Scandinavica, 59,* 685-697.

Castelnuovo, G., Giusti, E., Manzoni, G., Saviola, D., Gatti, A., Gabrielli, S. . . . Tamburn, S. (2016). Psychological treatments and psychotherapies in the neurorehabilitation of pain: Evidences and recommendations from the Italian Consensus Conference on Pain in Neurorehabilitation. *Frontiers in Psychology, 7,* 115.

Gierthmüller, J., & Baron, R. (2010). Komplexes regionales Schmerzsyndrom. In T. Standl, J. Schulte am Esch, R. D. Treede, M. Schäfer, & H. J. Bardenheuer (Eds.), *Akutschmerz, chronischer Schmerz, Palliativmedizin* (pp. 375-383). Stuttgart, Germany: Georg Thieme.

Jänig, W., & Baron, R. (2003). Complex regional pain syndrome: Mystery explained? *Lancet Neurology, 2,* 687-697.

Jensen, M. P. (2015). *Hypnose bei chronischem Schmerz: Ein Behandlungsmanual.* Heidelberg, Germany: Carl-Auer.

Lebon, J., Rongières, M., Apredoaei, C., Delclaux, S., & Mansat, P. (2017). Physical therapy under hypnosis for the treatment of patients with type 1 complex regional pain syndrome of the hand and wrist: Retrospective study of 20 cases. *Hand Surgery and Rehabilitation, 36,* 215-221.

Marinus, J., Moseley, G. L., Birklein, F., Baron, R., Maihöfner, C., Kingery, W. S., & van Hilten, J. J. (2010). Clinical features and pathophysiology of complex regional pain syndrome. *Neurology, 10,* 637–648.

Nkenke, S., (2012). Selbsthypnose bei komplexem regionalem Schmerzsyndrom (CRPS) Ein Fallbericht. *Hypnose-ZHH, 7,* 179-186

Sandroni, P., Benrud-Larson, L.M., McClelland, R.L., & Low, P. A. (2003). Complex regional pain syndrome type I: Incidence and prevalence in Olmsted County: A population-based study. *Pain, 103,* 199–207.

Veldman, P. H., Reynen, H. M., Arntz, I. E., & Goris, R. J. (1993). Signs and symptoms of reflex sympathetic dystrophy: Prospective study of 829 patients. *Lancet, 342,* 1012-1016.

CHAPTER 7

Hypnotic Suggestions Targeting Increased Comfort for Chronic Pain Management

Mark P. Jensen

Mark P. Jensen is a Professor and Vice Chair for Research in the Department of Rehabilitation Medicine, Seattle, Washington, USA. For the past 40 years, his clinical work and his research program have focused on developing interventions — including self-hypnosis treatment programs — that empower patients with chronic pain to get more control over pain and to decrease its impact on their lives. He has published over 500 articles and chapters and has facilitated hundreds of workshops throughout the world for clinicians to disseminate the knowledge gained from this work. He has received the Jay Haley Early Career Award for Innovative Contributions to Hypnosis from The International Society of Hypnosis, the Clark L. Hull Award for Scientific Excellence in Writing on Experimental Hypnosis from the American Journal of Clinical Hypnosis, the Wilbert E. Fordyce Clinical Investigator Award from the American Pain Society, and both the Distinguished Contributions to Scientific Hypnosis and the Distinguished Contributions to Professional Hypnosis awards from the American Psychological Association, Division 30, among other awards recognizing his contributions. His 2011 book, Hypnosis for Chronic Pain Management: Therapist

Guide, *published by Oxford University Press as part of their "Treatments that Work" series, won the Arthur Shapiro Award: Best Book on Hypnosis from the Society for Clinical and Experimental Hypnosis. In this chapter, Professor Jensen describes a number of empirically supported hypnotic suggestions that are designed to give patients with chronic pain skills they can use to increase and maintain their overall comfort.*

* * *

The purpose of this chapter is to provide clinicians with examples of hypnotic suggestions that have demonstrated efficacy for increasing comfort in a series of controlled clinical trials (e.g., Jensen et al., 2009a, 2009b, 2011; Mendoza et al., 2017; Tan et al., 2015). The chapter begins with an overview of some basic facts about chronic pain and provides useful ideas to keep in mind when using hypnosis to treat chronic pain problems. The bulk of the chapter includes specific scripts of suggestions that can be used to target improvement in a patient's comfort (i.e., a decrease in pain intensity).

Of course, adequate treatment for chronic pain should also include interventions that address the many symptoms that can be negatively impacted by pain, such as sleep quality, mood, and activity (Jensen, 2011). However, it is beyond the scope of this chapter to provide examples of hypnotic suggestions that target *all* of these important outcomes. Examples of hypnotic approaches and suggestions that target these important domains can be found elsewhere (Hammond, 1990; Jensen, 2011; Patterson, 2010).

Basic Facts about Chronic Pain and Hypnosis

In this section I review some basic facts about chronic pain and hypnosis that clinicians should keep in mind as they develop and provide hypnotic treatment. These include the following: (1) pain is the result of a complex interaction of activity in different parts of the brain and body; (2) pain is an output of the brain; (3) when providing hypnotic chronic pain treatment, it is useful to include a number of key strategies for enhancing both immediate and long-term treatment benefits.

Pain is the Result of a Complex Interaction of Activity in Different Parts of the Brain and Body

There are many areas of the body, including areas both outside and inside the central nervous system (CNS), that are involved in the creation of the pain experience (Jensen, 2008). These areas include the periphery (neuronal and chemical activity at the site[s] of injury, if injury is involved), the dorsal horn of the spinal cord (where sensory information from the periphery can be inhibited or magnified), the thalamus (a "relay station" that receives and then passes on to other areas of the brain the majority of sensory information from the periphery), the insula (where perceptions of the physical state of the body are processed), the anterior cingulate cortex (where emotional responses to sensations are processed), and the prefrontal cortex (where information about the meaning of sensations is processed). Moreover, the thalamus, insula, anterior cingulate cortex, and prefrontal cortex are hardwired to communicate directly with and influence each other.

The areas in the CNS that are involved in the creation of pain are part of the "pain matrix." Because of their direct connections, influencing activity in any *one* of these areas can potentially influence an individual's experience of pain. This means that clinicians have many possible physiological targets for hypnotic suggestions when the goal is to reduce pain. For example, they could focus on suggestions to alter activity in the periphery (e.g., "… and you can place the arm in a healing pool of water…") or in the dorsal horn and thalamus (part of the spinal-thalamic track, e.g., "... the brain can 'filter in' comfortable sensations and 'filter out' any sensations that are less than useful or helpful at this time..."). Suggestions can also target the insula (e.g., "... these sensations are, in fact, a signal that all is well, the body is working and doing what it needs to do..."), the anterior cingulate cortex (e.g., "... knowing that because all is well, and the body is doing what it needs to do to help you stay healthy, there is *nothing else you need to do* at this point, other than enjoy your life and those activities that are most important and meaningful to you..."), and the prefrontal cortex (e.g., "... understanding, more and more, the ways in which it is possible to live a life consistent with your most deeply held values, despite any challenges..."). Suggestions can also be made to nurture and enhance a "comfort matrix" and/or to disrupt connectivity and communication within the "pain matrix" (e.g., "... recalling a time when you felt so good, so strong, and so comfortable... becoming absorbed in this memory..." or "... noticing how body parts are so relaxed you even lose awareness of them... almost as if they belong to someone else... as they relax, and heal..." (see Jensen, 2008, 2011).

Because it is not always possible to know with certainty which areas and processes of the pain matrix are most involved in the pain experience of any one patient, clinicians would be wise to offer suggestions that target *each* of these areas for change, and then evaluate the efficacy of these suggestions for each specific patient. Tailoring the suggestions to each patient's unique situation in this way can enhance overall efficacy.

Pain is an Output of the Brain

Common language related to pain implies that pain is a "sensation" that is "felt" or "perceived" by the brain (i.e., an input). However, the state-of-the-science knowledge about pain confirms that pain is an experience that is *created* by the brain (i.e., an output). Of course, in the process of determining whether or not to create pain and which qualities to give it (magnitude, perceived location, sensory qualities, affective qualities), the brain takes into account numerous inputs from outside of the CNS (e.g., sensory and environmental cues) and information stored in the CNS (e.g., beliefs regarding the meaning of pain, previous learning).

In this way, pain is much more like an emotional reaction (such as anxiety, sadness, or optimism) than an estimate of the magnitude of a physical sensation (like the brightness of a light or the temperature of water). When a sensation or environmental cue—even a relatively weak one—is deemed by the brain to represent credible evidence that physical damage to the body is about to occur, the brain creates pain as a way to tell an individual to "watch out!" or "back off!" (Moseley & Butler, 2015). On the other hand, when a sensation or environmental cue—even a very strong one—is deemed irrelevant with respect to potential physical damage, the brain does not create pain.

Understanding pain as an output of the brain has very important implications with respect to the language used in hypnotic approaches for pain treatment. Specifically, it means that suggestions should avoid the idea that pain is something that is passively perceived rather than actively created. In other words, avoid saying "...when you feel pain..." or "...when you have pain..." or referring to the pain experience as "pain sensations." Instead, it is better to refer to the patient's "experience of pain" or "... when pain is created by the brain, usually in an attempt to protect you..."

Our understanding of the pain matrix also means that in general, the word "pain" should be avoided when offering suggestions during hypnosis, especially when offering suggestions for experiencing pain relief. When a suggestion is given to "reduce pain," the patient must then notice or even create pain in order to reduce it. Thus, suggestions for "pain reduction" are negative suggestions that can have the paradoxical effect of strengthening the very pain experience (and activity in the pain matrix) that the clinician and the patient are hoping to replace.

Perhaps one of the few times that the word "pain" should be uttered during a hypnotic suggestion is when the clinician seeks to help the patient understand at a deep level important facts about pain that can alter its meaning from something indicating damage to something less frightening. For example, "...knowing that your healthy brain and body create pain when needed to protect you, you can be aware that because you are healthy, you *will* experience pain in the future... and because you are healthy, you will also experience comfort... pain will come, and pain will go... that is how a healthy brain and body work... allowing you to stay healthy and protected... the brain and body can learn to create pain only when it is truly needed and useful..."

Strategies to Enhance Beneficial Outcomes

In order to enhance the immediate and long-term benefits of hypnotic treatments, clinicians should consider the following: (1) including a specific cue prior to each hypnosis session, (2) offering a variety of suggestions targeting a variety of outcomes, (3) making an audio recording of each session to facilitate regular home practice, (4) seeding key ideas throughout treatment, and (5) offering post-hypnotic suggestions to enhance both (a) regular practice of self-hypnosis and (b) the durability of treatment benefits.

Begin each session with a specific and consistent cue. When providing hypnosis treatment, I being each session by suggesting that the patient engage in a specific behavior. The cue I suggest most often is taking a deep breath (e.g., "...when you are ready... you can take a deep, relaxing breath... and hold it... hold it for a moment... and then let it go..."). But some patients might prefer a different cue, such as "... and when you are ready... you can allow the forefinger and thumb of your right hand to touch... and gently rub together..." or "... and when you are ready... you can be aware of your calm center, and then allow the eyes to close..." Any of these, and others, could be fine. However, the cue should be something that the patient has conscious control over and should be something that the patient can do anywhere easily (including in public) without appearing to be doing anything unusual.

Because the cue is offered at the beginning of *every* session, it becomes associated with that patient's usual hypnotic response, via classical conditioning. Moreover, because I audio record all of the sessions and encourage patients to listen to the recordings at least once every day, fairly quickly the patient will be able to use the cue as a means to achieve a rapid induction and for self-hypnosis. This gives the patient a new tool for using hypnosis to make other goal-related changes in automatic responses.

Here is a sample script of the cue suggestion used in many clinical trials in my research program (the specific cue suggestion is underlined in the script):

Clinician: Okay... just settle back... and allow the eyes to close.

Now... I'm going to talk to you for a while... all you have to do is listen to what I'm saying and allow yourself to have as pleasant an experience as you know how. Go ahead and adjust yourself to the most comfortable position you can.

[Observe participant. Wait until adjusting is completed before continuing.]

And remember, you can feel free to make any adjustments, at any time, to help yourself be comfortable, and this need not interrupt your concentration or your ability to maintain a deep state of comfortable relaxation.

Now, <u>go ahead and draw a deep, satisfying breath into your</u> <u>belly... and gently hold the breath for as long as it feels</u> <u>comfortable... *[wait about 2 seconds]* ... and now let it go.</u>

Repeat that process again, drawing a deep, satisfying breath into your belly... suspending, pausing... and letting it go.

Offer a variety of suggestions. I have already discussed the importance of offering patients with chronic pain suggestions that target each one of the components of the pain matrix; if clinicians limit themselves to a single "favorite" suggestion, there will most certainly be patients who will not respond well to treatment, because some of the patients' pain problems will be unrelated to the activity targeted by the one suggestion.

Thus, a key principal in all hypnosis treatment, emphasized consistently by master clinicians, is the importance of tailoring suggestions to each patient's particular situation. This often requires offering a variety of suggestions and then closely observing the patient's responses to each. Over time, the most effective and useful suggestions for each patient will be identified (Jensen, 2011).

Make an audio recording of each session. Some master clinicians express a hesitancy to provide patients with audio recordings of treatment sessions, expressing the concern that such recordings might make the patients more dependent on the clinician (or at least on the recordings) and/or that the patient may attribute the treatment gains to the recordings and not to the patient's own skills.

Another view is that patients benefit differently from different types of practice. For example, some may find that listening to the session recording regularly (e.g., daily) gives them the opportunity to hear the (empowering) hypnotic suggestions more often, allowing the most useful of these suggestions to "sink in" to a greater extent. Moreover, one of the post-hypnotic suggestions I often offer (which the patient would then listen to daily if he or she follows the advice to do so) is to encourage the patient to practice "… on your own, without the recording… as often as you find it useful… maybe three or more times every day, for a few minutes at a time…" and that this self-hypnosis practice without the recording can be initiated by the cue that precedes every session (i.e., "…by taking a nice deep breath…").

Interestingly, in our clinical trials, we found that the number of times the study participants listened to the recordings was unrelated to outcome; listening more often was not necessarily associated with better or worse outcomes. However, hypnotizability *was* associated with frequency of listening; individuals with higher levels of hypnotizability tended to practice more on their own without the recordings, while those with lower hypnotizability tended to listen to the recordings more often. This finding is consistent with the idea that patients "find their own path" towards improvement; our job as clinicians is to make as many paths available to the patients as possible. Providing audio recordings of the sessions makes one such path available.

Seeding ideas during the induction and throughout treatment. A common hypnotic technique is to "seed" the key ideas during the induction that will be the focus of suggestions during the session (Geary, 1994; Zeig, 1990; see also Weingarten et al., 2016). Of course, this seeding need not occur only during the induction; key ideas and the words associated with those ideas can be raised and mentioned as soon as the patient is first greeted, during discussions before formal hypnosis, during a formal hypnosis session, and after the hypnosis session.

With respect to chronic pain treatment, useful words and ideas include those that are inconsistent with pain, anxiety (especially with respect to anxiety regarding the meaning of increases in physical sensations), and inactivity. Useful ideas to seed also include important goals of chronic pain treatment, such as increases in patient empowerment, self-efficacy, hope, optimism, and a sense of calm acceptance. Words I frequently sprinkle into conversations with patients and into the inductions and hypnotic suggestions offered to patients include: "comfort/comfortable," "confident/ confidence," "calm," "strong/strength," "active," "hope," "looking forward," "carefree" and words reflecting personal choice and active involvement (e.g., "allow yourself," "adjust yourself").

So, for example, I might say as part of the formal induction something like:

Allow yourself **to have as** *pleasant* **an experience as you know how. Go ahead and** *adjust yourself* **to the most** *comfortable* **position you can...**

And remember, you can *feel free* **to make any adjustments, at any time, to help yourself remain** *relaxed and comfortable...*

Words seeding all of these ideas can be found throughout the scripts that are presented later in this chapter.

Offer post-hypnotic suggestions. The findings from our clinical trials indicate two types of benefits to self-hypnosis training. One benefit is relatively durable (and automatic) changes in how the brain processes nociception and other sensory information, such that the patient feels more comfort (i.e., less pain) throughout the days and weeks following treatment. These patients' brains have responded to the suggestions for greater comfort and now experience this comfort automatically, "...without having to do anything at all." The percentage of patients who report meaningful and durable reductions in pain varies as a function of pain diagnosis, from as low as about 20% for individuals with spinal cord injury-related pain (a particularly refractory pain problem) to as high as 80% for individuals with chronic headaches.

The second benefit described by patients in response to the hypnosis treatment, is that they have learned a "skill" and now have a "tool" to manage pain when they wish to feel more comfortable. Patients who describe this benefit report that they use self-hypnosis (e.g., starting with the cue) when they wish to feel more comfortable at the moment. They say that when they do so, they experience more comfort that can last anywhere from the time they remain "in trance" to as long as many hours after they engage in the experience. The great majority (usually 80% or more) of patients describe this treatment benefit and report that they continue to use self-hypnosis for pain management. Patients who use self-hypnosis in this way appear to be using self-hypnosis as a type of effective analgesic (although it is an analgesic without negative side effects!) that produces meaningful, short-term improvement in pain.

Therefore, I usually provide post-hypnotic suggestions to utilize these two naturally occurring benefits. Thus, at the very end of each session, after the clinical suggestions, but before alerting, I might say something like:

And now we have reached the time to extend what has been most useful to you in this session

> *[In other words, a post-hypnotic suggestion that they now have a skill they can use to experience comfort on-command.]*

You are learning new ways of helping yourself to feel more comfortable... more confident... and stronger... and the more you practice, however you find yourself doing it... perhaps listening to the recordings... or practicing on your own several times every day by taking that nice deep breath... or perhaps both, whatever you find most helpful...

Your mind will be able to use these skills, automatically, so that you can create comfort and relaxation and an inner strength, whenever you need it.

And the benefits you create for yourself... you can take these into the rest of your day, and your daily life...

Any time **you want to feel more comfortable, to allow yourself to again experience the benefits of today's session... all you ever have to do... is to take a very deep, very satisfying breath, and hold it, hold it for a moment... and then let it go.**

And any of the comfortable feelings and benefits, any helpful responses that you have created for yourself in this

session, will come washing over you... naturally, easily, and automatically.

These benefits can linger and last beyond the sessions... for minutes... hours... days... and years. Becoming an *automatic* and *permanent* part of your comfort. ... And these benefits will last for *as long* as they continue to be helpful.

> [*In other words, a post-hypnotic suggestion that improvements in comfort will be durable.*]

Sample Scripts for Increasing Comfort

Most formal hypnosis sessions begin with an induction, then provide specific clinical suggestions that target changes consistent with the patient's treatment goals. As mentioned previously, when treating chronic pain the clinician should almost always consider including suggestions that target multiple aspects of the pain matrix, as well as the multiple quality of life domains important for long-term adjustment to chronic pain; chronic pain treatment involves more than just pain reduction (Jensen, 2011).

However, the factor that motivates the majority of patients to seek treatment is high levels of uncontrollable pain intensity and the suffering associated with this pain intensity. Many, if not most, patients seek pain reduction as a primary treatment goal. Thus, it is often useful to begin treatment by offering suggestions that are most likely to have immediate and large effects on pain reduction, especially when this is the primary treatment goal of the patient.

Here I present a variety of scripts that target pain reduction as a treatment goal. They include: (1) creating and changing a metaphor for pain, (2) general permissive suggestions for comfort, (3) suggestions for psychological analgesia, (4) suggestions for changing sensation, (5) suggestions for making reassuring pain-related thoughts automatic, and (6) age progression for comfort and confidence. All of these suggestions are adapted from those used in a series of past and ongoing clinical trials with proven efficacy (e.g., Jensen et al., 2009a, 2009b; Jensen et al., 2011; Mendoza et al., 2017; Tan et al., 2015).

Two or even three of these suggestions might be offered in the same session, although I generally do not offer more than three during any one session. Often, if the patient has identified a "favorite" or "most effective" (so far) suggestion from a previous session, I will include that favorite suggestion along with one or two new suggestions during the very next treatment session. That way, the patient gets to hear a different version of a favorite suggestion (which can build on its beneficial effects) while also being offered a new experience which has the potential to become a new favorite.

Over time, because each session is audio recorded, the patient builds a "library" of recordings that includes suggestions tailored to his or her particular pain problem.

Creating and Changing a Metaphor for Pain

The mind's ability to alter the experience and the meaning of an event via the use of metaphor is well established in the hypnosis community (e.g., Kirmayer, 1988; Steckler, 1992). What follows is a classic example of this technique.

Clinician: You can notice that something very interesting is happening... that as your comfort grows... any other feelings or sensations just seem to be drifting farther and farther away. You might even imagine any bothersome sensations as an image... perhaps as leaves floating down a stream... or perhaps as a burning fire... I do not know what color they are, or what the image is... but you do.

You can notice the details of the image, watching as those details change. Perhaps they are floating slowly away, drifting down the stream. ... Or you might see them as the embers of a fire, slowly burning out... the colors of the embers slowly dimming, becoming more cool and comfortable.... Leaves floating down a stream, or embers becoming cool and comfortable... or some other creative and interesting image that changes... whatever change you experience, that change can be for the better... more comfortable, and perhaps smaller and smaller... *[Pause 10 seconds]*.

And now, maybe you can take these images of any feelings or sensations that are diminishing, and place then into a strong, thick, insulated box. Right into the box...

And you can see yourself placing the lid on the box, and securing it.... Muffling the sensations... *[Pause]* and then putting this box into a second very secure box, and placing the lid on the second box... *[Pause]* securing it. The sensations are in there, but... muffled... softer somehow... safe and secure...

And putting this second box into yet another box. ... And again, closing the lid. Securing it. Nothing can get out.

And then, and you can use your creativity here, imagine sending the box far, far away. ... Maybe deep into space... maybe across the ocean... but really imagine it going away... picturing it. Far, far away. ... So much easier to ignore now...

And with those sensations so far away, it is even easier to feel the comfort of every breath. So easy to let yourself daydream about a peaceful place, to imagine a happy time in your life or a happy time you'd like to have. Letting yourself feel free, right now, to just let your mind wander...

General Permissive Suggestions for Comfort

Many patients are able to access very creative strategies for creating comfort and this ability appears to increase following a hypnotic induction. In order to maximize this ability, clinicians should offer general, permissive suggestions; providing an overall goal (in this case, comfort) but without necessarily providing specific strategies for how the patient might achieve the goal. Utilizing the patient's creative processes can be very empowering.

Clinician: Such a pleasure to be here, with nothing to bother you and nothing to disturb you. With every breath you take, breathing comfort in and tension out, just notice how naturally you feel more and more comfort. And any feelings of discomfort seem to have lessened and maybe even have disappeared altogether, like some memory long forgotten or like something you have stored away but no longer need to have in your immediate awareness.

Letting each breath you take... contribute to your comfort and well-being.

You are training your nervous system so that it is possible to be more aware of pleasant sensations and helpful feelings, so aware of pleasant sensations and feelings, in fact, that it is hard to notice any other type of feelings. Noticing, just noticing, how the mind focuses more and more on these feelings of calmness, comfort, and relaxation.

And I wonder if you might be curious about just how absorbed you can become in noticing these comfortable sensations... or whatever other pleasant feelings you notice;

how good this feels. And your ability to create these comfortable sensations is growing, and becoming more and more automatic all the time.

Not only that, but the more you notice these good feelings, the better you feel emotionally... calmer and calmer... more and more hopeful and confident. ... You can just... feel *good*...

[Pause about 5 seconds].

A Suggestion for Psychological Analgesia

Virtually everyone has some memory of taking an analgesic, such as aspirin, for pain. Many people have had dental work performed using a local anesthetic such as Novocain and so have an association between the application of the anesthetic and the sensory experience of numbness or lack of pain. It is possible to utilize these memories and experiences to create comfort.

Clinician: You are now going to imagine a powerful treatment that you can use to help you feel more comfortable in any areas of the body that you wish. You can imagine that you are applying *something* to the area of the body that you would like to feel more comfortable... it can be anything you like: a sensation of warmth, or coolness... *[Pause]*, a color... *[Pause]*, a cloth moistened with a healing medicine, that is just the right temperature... *[Pause]*, or a powerful liquid medicine or gel... *[Pause]*, whatever feels just right for you...

Now, experience the areas in the body that you would like to feel more comfortable being completely surrounded... or filled... with this treatment. It brings on a sensation of comfort... a pleasant sensation of comfort... picture these comfortable feelings spreading through that area.

And now you might notice how naturally, how easily, the comfortable sensations can make those areas feel *even more pleasant*, maybe decreasing some sensations from that area, or maybe even noticing some sensations disappear. Notice how the *pleasant* and *comfortable* sensations just wash over everything. Such a pleasure to be able to experience... to make real... such comfort.

These areas of your body are feeling more and more comfortable as the treatment does its work and the feelings of comfort spread. This powerful and *long-lasting* treatment is doing its job. Such positive effects... greater comfort... a sense of calmness and of confidence... and it can last for hours... and, you might be pleasantly surprised... even days! As you gain more experience, the treatment will become even *more* powerful and *more* effective... and can last for as long as you need.

Your ability to give yourself comfort is growing and becoming a part of who you are. You have the opportunity, now, to really enjoy the comfort of these sensations... to feel comfortable and at ease... so very comfortable and at ease.

Suggestions for Decreasing the Intensity of Sensations

Rarely, if ever, do sensations actually remain stable over time. Moreover, even when or if the actual sensory input is stable, our awareness of the magnitude of that input varies from moment to moment, depending on what else may require our attention or how important the system views that input. It is possible for patients to utilize this natural variability by first noticing it and by then allowing the brain to learn how to minimize the awareness of input that may "no longer be useful."

Clinician: And as you sink down again into a deeper, deeper state of comfort, you begin to realize that it is the mind that creates sensations out of all that input. There is constant input going into our brain, although sometimes there is more, and sometimes there is less. ... There are also constant sensations occurring in the body; one sensation appears... only to be followed by another, and then by another. One thought occurs, followed by another.

We have *so many* sensations, thoughts, and feelings... what we actually experience, what we are aware of, is just a matter of what we are focused on. We are constantly changing moment to moment... what we focus on can change moment to moment, so the sensations, the thoughts, the feelings that we are aware of change as well, right along with us...

And isn't it interesting that you will be able to find yourself, as you are now, observing your thoughts, feelings, sensations, just coming and going, arriving, passing. ... Maybe it will be as if you can see your feelings floating down a river on some leaves as you observe them... noticing that even if you wanted to, you couldn't stop the sensations from drifting away...

Sensations coming, sensations going, just observing them without being attached to them. Leaves floating away and any discomfort with them. The river floating away into the distance and the intensity becoming less and less. ... Just noticing how they become dimmer and dimmer and just move away. ... So very peaceful... so comfortable. ... Not a care in the world and not attached to anything that happens...

Suggestions for Making Reassuring Pain-Related Thoughts Automatic

As indicated previously, the meaning given to sensations has a significant impact on whether—and how much—pain will be experienced. Thus, an important strategy for reducing pain intensity is to suggest comforting thoughts about pain and to instill confidence that these thoughts will eventually become automatic.

Clinician: Perhaps you might wonder how the things you learn and practice somehow happen to become automatic... helpful thoughts about your pain life that once took some practice to learn and now just seem natural and effortless because you have thought about them enough...

Isn't it interesting that at least certain thoughts about your body, your sensations, and your coping now seem to occur naturally... almost without any effort at all.

Sometimes it is so easy to forget that... *you have a vault of precious, useful, adaptive, helpful, and reassuring thoughts about your body, your sensations, and what you can do to cope* **that you have developed over the years...**

So often it is simply a matter of calling on these powerful resources. In fact, you are probably aware of some specific thoughts that are very useful and reassuring to you, even now. ... Perhaps the idea that...

[Here, the clinician can offer a thought about pain that the patient has mentioned before and that the clinician judges to be particularly helpful. Thoughts like, "Pain comes and pain goes...", "I am able to live my life consistent with my values

no matter what sensations I have...", or "I am learning ways
to feel more comfortable, more of the time."]

With the mind drifting now... go ahead and notice what types of helpful thoughts you have learned to experience about your physical sensations *[Pause]*. Maybe thoughts like "This too shall pass"... or "Deep inside, my body will know how to help me feel more comfortable"... or "I can focus on what brings me comfort and joy." Just allow the mind to drift... and now drift to the thought that you have already decided will be helpful to you right now...

These thoughts are there, in your mind. They can come forward when needed, like a trusted friend, to reassure you and bring you comfort, just when they are needed and most appropriate...

One of the most amazing gifts of our brain is for it to be able to detect and transform negative thoughts into positive ones, and we can simply trust its ability to do that; when we are offered a thought or idea that is less than helpful, when we are in a good relationship with our brain, the brain can simply ignore them. They are of no benefit to anyone.

Yes, we know about the potential of the brain to transform thoughts that might be less than helpful into truly reassuring and helpful ones. What is much more compelling about this is the notion of a part of your brain that operates at a much higher level—a noble screener of thoughts and ideas. That indeed, this part of your brain seems to have the wisdom to screen out less helpful thoughts early, to understand the differences between more helpful and less helpful thoughts, and to transform them as needed and as appropriate for your well-being and comfort...

Age Progression for Comfort and Confidence

Finally, among the most effective suggestions that we use in our clinical trials (and one that patients almost uniformly say is among their favorites) is an age progression suggestion, adapted largely from Moshe Torem's work (Torem, 1992, 2017).

And as you continue to experience yourself in your favorite place, I wonder what it is you can see... if you are outdoors or if you can see out a window, you see the color of the sky... so intense... so real to you... and the temperature is just right... feeling so at peace...

And now... you can see a future version of yourself... maybe a few weeks or few months older... you can see that you are feeling even better than you do now. ... You have met some important goal or goals... perhaps you are stronger in some ways... perhaps more comfortable and confident... perhaps you can see this person walking towards you... or maybe standing or sitting with you. ... Yes, it is you, but it is you in the future.

This person might be several weeks older, or even a few months older... but you can see... you are even more comfortable than you are now... even more relaxed... and even more able to put yourself into a stage of deep comfort and relaxation.

Notice what you see in your future self. How you look... how wonderful you feel. And you can tell... just by looking, that you are doing better... perhaps you are stronger... perhaps more fit... you have made important steps towards goals that are most meaningful to you... and you have succeeded.

You can see how wonderful you feel. ... Seeing your future self very vividly now... perhaps there is a smile on your face... the way you move...

And now... you can experience yourself as *becoming* that future self. Experience your present self and future self, becoming one. And you can feel the greater comfort, the greater confidence... *experience* yourself as having made real progress towards your personal goals.

Looking back at your current self, and perhaps becoming aware of the steps you took to achieve the progress you have made, I wonder what reassuring and helpful ideas and thoughts you have for your current self. *[Pause about 10 seconds.]* To the extent that those thoughts are helpful, and as long as they continue to be helpful, let them sink deeply into your mind, so that they can always be available when you need them... to remind and reassure...

And now, allowing yourself to come back into your current self.... The future and present now blended into one... anything that you discovered or found helpful now has become part of you. Perhaps a way of thinking... a way of feeling... greater confidence... greater hope... perhaps a sense of hopeful excitement...

References

Geary, B. B. (1994). Seeding responsiveness to hypnotic processes. In J. K. Zeig (Ed.), *Ericksoniam methods: The essence of the story* (pp. 315-332). New York, NY: Routledge.

Hammond, D. C. (Ed.) (1990). *Handbook of hypnotic suggestions and metaphors*. New York, NY: Norton & Company.

Jensen, M. P. (2008). The neurophysiology of pain perception and hypnotic analgesia: Implications for clinical practice. *American Journal of Clinical Hypnosis, 51*, 123-148.

Jensen, M. P. (2011). *Hypnosis for chronic pain management: Therapist guide.* New York, NY: Oxford University Press.

Jensen, M. P., Barber, J., Romano, J. M., Hanley, M. A., Raichle, K. A., Molton, I. R., ... Patterson, D. R. (2009a). Effects of self-hypnosis training and EMG biofeedback relaxation training on chronic pain in persons with spinal-cord injury. *International Journal of Clinical and Experimental Hypnosis, 57,* 239-268.

Jensen, M. P., Barber, J., Romano, J. M., Molton, I. R., Raichle, K. A., Osborne, T. L., ... Patterson, D. R. (2009b). A comparison of self-hypnosis versus progressive muscle relaxation in patients with multiple sclerosis and chronic pain. *International Journal of Clinical and Experimental Hypnosis, 57,* 198-221.

Jensen, M. P., Ehde, D. M., Gertz, K. J., Stoelb, B. L., Dillworth, T. M., Hirsh, A. T., ... Kraft, G. H. (2011). Effects of self-hypnosis training and cognitive restructuring on daily pain intensity and catastrophizing in individuals with multiple sclerosis and chronic pain. *International Journal of Clinical and Experimental Hypnosis, 59,* 45-63.

Kirmayer, L. J. (1988). Word magic and the rhetoric of common sense: Erickson's metaphors for mind. *International Journal of Clinical and Experimental Hypnosis, 36,* 157-172.

Mendoza, M. E., Capafons, A., Gralow, J. R., Syrjala, K. L., Suarez-Rodriguez, J. M., Fann, J. R., & Jensen, M. P. (2017). Randomized controlled trial of the Valencia model of waking hypnosis plus CBT for pain, fatigue, and sleep management in patients with cancer and cancer survivors. *Psychooncology, 26,* 1832-1838.

Moseley, G. L., & Butler, D. S. (2015). Fifteen Years of Explaining Pain: The Past, Present, and Future. *Journal of Pain, 16*, 807-813.

Patterson, D. R. (2010). *Clinical hypnosis for pain control.* Washington, DC: American Psychological Assocation.

Steckler, J. T. (1992). The utilization of hypnosis in psychotherapy: metaphor and transformation. *Psychiatric Medicine, 10*, 41-50.

Tan, G., Rintala, D. H., Jensen, M. P., Fukui, T., Smith, D., & Williams, W. (2015). A randomized controlled trial of hypnosis compared with biofeedback for adults with chronic low back pain. *European Journal of Pain, 19*, 271-280.

Torem, M. S. (1992). "Back from the future": a powerful age-progression technique. *American Journal of Clinical Hypnosis, 35*, 81-88.

Torem, M. S. (2017). Future-focused therapeutic strategies for integrative health. *International Journal of Clinical and Experimental Hypnosis, 65*, 353-378.

Weingarten, E., Chen, Q., McAdams, M., Yi, J., Hepler, J., & Albarracin, D. (2016). From primed concepts to action: A meta-analysis of the behavioral effects of incidentally presented words. *Psychological Bulletin, 142*, 472-497.

Zeig, J. K. (1990). Seeding. In J. K. Zeig & S. G. Gilligan (Eds.), *Brief therapy: Myths, methods, and metaphors* (pp. 221-246). New York, NY: Brunner/Mazel.

CHAPTER 8

Optimizing the Efficacy of Hypnosis for Chronic Pain Treatment

Shigeru Matsuki

Shigeru Matsuki is a clinical psychologist and professor in the Professional Graduate School of Clinical Psychology at Kagoshima University, Kagoshima, Japan. He is the current chair of the Japanese Society of Clinical Hypnosis and executive director of the Japanese Society of Hypnosis. Based on his more than 40 years of experience in the application of clinical hypnosis, he regularly applies hypnosis in his psychotherapy practice and studies its effects in both hospital and private practice settings. His current field of practice is broad, ranging from the treatment of psychiatric symptoms (e.g., anxiety disorder, dissociative disorder, personality disorder), psychosomatic disorders (IBS, chronic pain), a variety of additional medical conditions (e.g., type 1 diabetes, dystonia, juvenile Parkinson's disease), and general stress in both adults and children. He is the author of numerous articles and books, including many on the topic of stress management in children, as well as publications regarding his theory of "the space of hypnotic trance," which is a model for how hypnotherapy has its healing effects.

* * *

Over the last several decades, numerous randomized clinical trials have demonstrated the efficacy of standardized hypnotic treatments (e.g., Whorwell et al., 1984; Jensen & Patterson, 2006; Whitehead, 2006). Hypnosis is now recommended as an effective treatment for irritable bowel syndrome (IBS) (Whorwell et al., 1984) and acute pain (Adachi et al., 2014; Jensen, 2016). In Japan, many hypnotic techniques for both chronic and acute pain reduction have been developed and taught; techniques which are supported by recent scientific findings (e.g., Mizutani, 2006, 2015a; 2015b).

While standardized and protocol-driven interventions are required in order to evaluate treatment efficacy in clinical trials, most experienced clinicians would not choose to use a standardized protocol with any patient. Symptoms—including pain—are influenced by many psychosocial factors; they are "multi-layered" and each patient is unique. The presentation and causes of symptoms are often quite diverse, even when patients carry the same diagnosis.

This diversity can make it challenging to effectively address our patients' symptoms; using a standardized procedure will not always give us the beneficial outcome that we expect (Matsuki, 2005; Ogiso et al., 2015). For each patient, we must consider how to best address the inherent limitations of standardized techniques. Thus, although empirical findings based on standardized strategies are important for developing and evaluating new hypnotic techniques, and can provide important new data which can be used to improve outcome, it remains important for each clinician to consider how to best use these research findings for each individual patient.

In this chapter, I will begin by presenting a case example of a patient with chronic pain for whom none of the standardized hypnotic procedures had been effective. This will be followed by a description of how I improved the patient's symptoms using ideas for optimizing hypnosis. My hope is that this chapter will provide an illustrative example of how clinicians can bridge the gap between evidence-based treatments (i.e., using standardized protocols) and creative clinical work in order to optimize their techniques to meet the needs of each patient. The case is based on one presented in a symposium at the 2005 Japanese Society of Clinical Hypnosis meeting (titled, "Learning from Mistakes," Matsuki, 2005).

Case Overview

This case is a 36-year-old man presenting with continuous pain over his entire body. Ultimately, treatment involved focusing on the patient's own words and the messages underlying these words, and utilizing catalepsy to facilitate the identification of effective suggestions.

The patient had injured his spinal cord in an automobile accident two years prior to our first interview. His initial complaint was of a minor pain accompanied by a light numbness in his neck and right upper arm. An examination at a university hospital, including an MRI scan, showed no indications of serious structural damage; therefore, no treatment was initially offered.

Meanwhile, the patient's pain started to get worse. The patient then sought help in a nearby medical clinic. Despite multiple biomedical treatments, including nerve blocks, analgesic medications, physical therapy, acupuncture, and moxibustion (a traditional Chinese medicine treatment, consisting of burning dried mugwort on or near the patient's skin), the pain continued to worsen, making the patient unable to work.

The patient's primary care physician concluded that psychosocial factors (such as anxiety and the stress of continual pain) and troubles with his work colleagues were aggravating the pain. He was referred to my practice, with the idea that psychotherapy to address these issues may reduce or help him to better manage the pain. The referring physician thought that autogenic training or hypnosis might be especially effective in this case.

Initial presentation

In our first session, he not only complained that the pain had spread widely throughout his body, but he had a "way" of describing the pain that was rather distinctive, indicating a great complexity to the symptom. For example, he initially described the pain as having qualities commonly associated with neuropathic pain (i.e., pain related to nerve damage or dysfunction; that is, it had a "cutting" quality, that light touch on the skin was enough to cause the pain, and that he experienced a tingling sensation on the surface of the skin). As therapy continued, he used additional words which seemed to not only associate directly with his pain experience, but also indirectly communicated the difficult situation he was living in (e.g., he once explained that "the temperature difference between me and my surroundings stimulates the pain"). On the surface, this statement indicates that the change in the surrounding temperature was functioning as a direct stimulus for pain; but at the same time, he seemed to be indirectly communicating that he feels "left out in the cold" by others. This could have been another stimulus which negatively influenced his pain experience.

I assumed that he was unconsciously describing the psychosocial factors contributing to his pain. Over time, he added a visceral word to describe his pain, saying that it "...felt as if my body was being squashed on the inside." In addition, he began to sweat excessively during work, and he explained that this was the primary reason he could no longer go to work, because it interfered with his filing duties.

Course of therapy

As the patient's primary care physician recommended, I first provided autogenic training and relaxation-based hypnosis. However, this resulted in worsening the pain and induced a very strong negative emotional reaction. More specifically, I provided a relaxation-based hypnosis session after a brief psychoeducation as a standardized procedure. For many individuals with chronic pain, relaxation can easily be achieved with such a procedure and is often associated with a marked reduction in pain. This can help boost outcome expectancies and self-efficacy (as relaxation is a skill that can be easily learned), both of which can facilitate beneficial outcomes.

However, in this case, as I continued the induction, the patient started complaining that the tingling sensations on the surface of his skin were getting stronger. He also started to complain of nausea, and that his hypersensitivity was also getting worse. He requested that we stop the induction.

He later explained that at first he had been feeling comfortable, but as the induction continued his skin started to feel hot, which brought on memories of the pain, the tingling skin, and a sense of feeling hot when people touched him. He could not help but cry. He ended by saying, "It's no good relaxing; I must stay focused at all times." (The actual word in the conversation was "ki-wo yurumeru to roku-na koto-ga nai."

The phrase *"ki-wo yurumeru"* is usually used as an idiom for *"stay focused"* in Japanese but is a body-related phrase that describes experiencing tension in one's body.)

He had a similar response at the second and third sessions, when autogenic training was attempted. Although he did not have a strong negative emotional response during these sessions, the uncomfortable physical sensations returned.

It seemed as if not only were we making no progress, but each session was making his pain worse. He had told me that he could not "settle down." ("Settle down" is *"mi o katameru"* in Japanese and is an idiom for "getting married," but its literal meaning in Japanese is "to stiffen your body.") He used this phrase in its literal meaning, at least at the conscious level. However, the idiomatic meaning of the phrase was enough for me to understand that his was a particularly complicated situation.

Based on his response to the initial sessions, it was clear that simple relaxation was not going to be beneficial; in fact, this approach clearly interfered with his ability to regulate his emotions. During the fourth session, we discussed the entire context of his pain problem in greater detail. He discussed many issues, such as his stressful work environment, ongoing difficulties with his boss, impatience with himself for being unable to work regularly, and his marriage being delayed. The words and phrases he used most often to describe his situation included "always tingling," "constraining," "making me heat up," "gets on my nerves," "could not be settled," and "unstable."

To help identify a useful path forward, I utilized catalepsy during the induction phase. This was a technique I had previously found useful when treating a patient with borderline personality disorder, with whom catalepsy had been useful to manage anxiety and other uncontrollable emotional responses (Matsuki, 2008).

I induced catalepsy in his left arm and left leg with his eyes open and I suggested that he experience pain reduction by anesthesia in the area (a specific script showing one way to induce catalepsy is provided later in the chapter). In response, the patient said that he did not feel the tingling sensations when touched, did not "heat up," and he found it interesting (i.e., this did not interfere with emotional regulation) to see the area become stiff. I further suggested that, as he experienced anesthesia in the areas that are sometimes uncomfortable (again, the session transcript later in the chapter provides examples of these suggestions), he could feel all the *other* parts of the body relaxing.

During hypnosis, he experienced pain reduction primarily in the area where anesthesia was produced; at the same time, he was able to feel relaxed in other parts of his body without the negative effects associated with suggestions for relaxing the painful areas. Although pain did return after this session (i.e., this single session did not "cure" his pain), it was clear that we had found a path forward.

We continued using this approach in sessions five and six, but with something more. This time, after the induction of catalepsy, I suggested that the patient gradually but progressively recover from the catalepsy at his own pace, feeling any tension releasing step by step. The goal here was to help him to "accept" the pain experience which was temporarily dissociated from his body by catalepsy. In other words, accepting pain at his own pace meant that he was gradually discovering the amount of pain which he could control on his own.

Session seven was done the same way. He experienced both a sense of his body loosening and of his pain reducing. He described the experience as, "It's getting warm" (i.e., rather than "heating up"), "not tingling, but fluffy," "I can sense the flow" (i.e., rather than "feeling stuck"). The pain had not totally disappeared, but his words indicated that he was now understanding that the pain was controllable. This approach was used for the next four sessions.

Reflecting the progress of the therapy, in session 12, when he talked about his boss (who continued to harass him), he noted that the boss *also* had problems. This was a clear shift of tone from focusing on blaming his boss to exhibiting an ability to show empathy for his boss and also understand his own role in the interactions. Thus, he began to also experience feelings of guilt.

Assuming that his complex feelings were having a negative impact on his pain, encouraging him to express hostile feelings about his boss in a direct manner was not likely to be effective. Instead, I thought it would be more effective to help him withhold his ambivalent feelings about his pain, which I assumed would also increase his ability to control his feelings toward his boss. This could provide a way to help him increase his ability to control pain by (1) accepting pain at his own pace and by (2) being able to experience rapid anesthesia when needed.

So, in this session (session 12), before we finished practicing loosening the catalepsy, I suggested that (1) he would be able to recover from/loosen the catalepsy on his own when he needed and that (2) he could achieve catalepsy on his own whenever he needed. In fact, at this point he noted that he had already done so and he felt confident in his ability to achieve catalepsy when he needed in order to gain rapid control over his pain. He did not feel the need at this point to practice achieving catalepsy further.

As can be seen from this case example, it is critical to listen carefully to and focus on the patient's words, as well as the unspoken messages behind them (Kandabashi, 2011). These words can then be incorporated into the induction and clinical suggestions as a way to optimize efficacy for each patient's unique situation.

In most, if not all cases of chronic pain, the psychosocial factors which contribute to the patient's symptoms interact in a multi-layered and complex fashion (Matsuki, 2012). These factors are communicated to us by both the surface and the deeper messages behind the patient's own words; they tell the story of the patient's pain experience. These principles are clear in this case, where factors such as being oversensitive in interpersonal relationships, suppressed hostility to others (especially to his boss), and a worrying feeling created by the uncertainty of his own future, were all communicated by the patient's words and the messages behind them. The goal here was to optimize the hypnotic suggestions to meet this particular patient's needs and to interact with all of the multiple factors contributing to his pain and suffering.

A New Paradigm for Research in Clinical Hypnosis

In order for hypnosis research to make important contributions to our scientific understanding of its efficacy and mechanisms, it is necessary to gather precise, objective data from and about research study participants and be able to generalize the findings to the population of patients who could benefit from hypnosis treatments. Evidence-based approaches require evidence, and randomized controlled trials evaluating the efficacy of standardized treatment protocols are important and necessary for establishing efficacy.

However, no patient is the average patient; each one is unique. Clinicians must therefore be flexible in adapting the treatments which have been shown to be effective "on average" to each patient's unique situation. We need to optimize our techniques to address the complex and multi-layered psychosocial factors that contribute to each patient's symptom presentation and overall adjustment.

As the specific mechanisms that underlie the efficacy of hypnosis remain unclear, outcome is strongly influenced by each clinician's experience, skills, and flexibility. The approach I took in this case (using catalepsy as an initial technique to teach self-control, based a single previous case where this was effective) is not a strategy commonly used in pain management, and it remains possible that there are other techniques which might have been even more effective. However, it appeared to have been beneficial in this case, providing a turning point for this patient.

To what extent might a similar approach be useful for other individuals who do not respond well to standard relaxation inductions or autogenic training? Such a question would need to be addressed by clinical research that develops a standardized protocol for this approach and then evaluates this protocol systematically in a sample of individuals with chronic pain (perhaps in a specific sample who report increased pain with relaxation procedures).

This case history illustrates how clinicians are in an excellent position to contribute valuable direction to research. Initial ideas regarding treatments to be evaluated could come from clinicians working in the field whose work is, by definition, one of discovering new, unique, approaches to the problems presented by their patients. In this way, the field benefits greatly from the discoveries and insights made by experienced clinicians. Case reports are an excellent way to disseminate these discoveries to other clinicians and clinical researchers. Knowledge gained from both innovative clinical approaches (which can be disseminated via case reports) and rational evidence from well-conduced clinical trials are complementary. The treatment of pain could greatly benefit from a more direct interaction between clinician and researcher, building together both a new paradigm for research, and new treatments that optimize efficacy for each unique patient.

Script for Utilizing Catalepsy to Facilitate Chronic Pain Management

As described previously, both autogenic training and relaxation-based hypnosis were not only ineffective for this patient, but resulted in a worsening of the patient's pain. Therefore, I used a three-step procedure to utilize hypnotically induced catalepsy to reduce pain.

In the first step, I suggested hypnotic catalepsy to produce a light anesthesia to reduce pain; furthermore, letting the patient feel that he is both safe and secure, not distracted by the pain.

In the second step, based on this sense of safety, and in order to allow the patient to become relaxed at his own pace, I suggested a gradual and stepwise relaxation in the areas of the body where catalepsy was present, with a goal of producing greater reductions in pain.

In the third and final step, I taught the patient how to progressively relax himself by asking him to practice recovering from the catalepsy state on his own.

Here I present the key portions of the induction and suggestions. There is not enough room to provide the entire script. Therefore, a brief introduction will be presented, followed by an explanation to help understand the overview.

Step One: Induction of Catalepsy to Produce Light Anesthesia

Before beginning the induction, an explanation should be given regarding what hypnotic catalepsy is and what effect can be expected. Then, the induction begins with a careful consideration not to interfere with the patient's concentration.

With the patient instructed to keep his or her eyes open, the clinician induces catalepsy in the left arm and left leg and suggests anesthesia for pain reduction. It is important for the patient to be fully aware of the experience, so the induction is made with eyes open and suggestions for high levels of concentration. The clinician sits a little bit closer to the patient than for the usual hypnosis session. The clinician begins by asking the patient to put his or her left hand on the left thigh.

Clinician: Okay, now please make a fist with your left hand, with only your thumb sticking straight up. All the other fingers should be gripped tight. Do you understand?

Patient: [Nods]

Clinician: Now, take a close look at your thumbnail. As you look at that nail, the other four fingers will slowly increase in tension. [Pause] Yes, focusing on that nail will bring tension to those other four fingers. ... They begin to come together as one, becoming stiffer and stronger. You actually see the hand becoming more tense... more and more... and at some point, you will see that all five fingers have become stiff... without you even noticing exactly when this occurred.... You can see for yourself. ... Do you have a sense

that the fingers are so strongly stiff... so rigid that you are unable to move them?

Patient: [Nods.]

Clinician: If you feel that you can move them, go ahead and try. Try to move the fingers.

[The patient tries to move the hand but catalepsy is present and so the patient is unable to do so.]

Patient: I cannot open my hand with my thumb stuck straight up. This is an interesting feeling. [Pause.] Can't... move. [Pause.] My hand is getting cold.

Clinician: Good. You can notice that the fingers are not opening, right?

Patient: [Agrees.]... [Pause.] My hand is cold, and I feel a little numbness.

Clinician: You can see the catalepsy in your hands and might be feeling rather *safe* and *secure*.

[Including suggestions for feeling safe and secure is an important component of my method.]

Patient: [Agrees.]... [Pause.] Not only the hand, but my thigh is also getting cold.

Clinician: Good. Let yourself feel those sensations as much as you want. [Pause.] Now, do you mind if I touch your hand? [Patient nods, indicating agreement.] How does it feel now being touched?

Patient: Hmm... [Pause.] I don't feel any tingling sensation. It doesn't heat up. It's interesting that it's stiff in a nice way. I don't know if it hurts or doesn't hurt...

[The induction continues...]

As the procedure continues, the clinician induces anesthesia via catalepsy, and the patient experiences a reduction in his cutaneous pain sensations. Then, and as a second step, as the clinician suggests ongoing catalepsy in the painful area, the clinician then suggests relaxation in all the *other* parts of the body.

Step Two: Stepwise Relaxation and Pain Reduction in Other Areas of the Body

Clinician: Now, as you can feel the cold and numb state of your left hand, at the same time you also feel an absence of tingling sensations...

Patient: *[Nods.]... [Pause.]*

Clinician: And as you continue, you may notice that your right hand is free...

[Clinician observes the patient very closely with plans to only continue if a positive response occurs.]

Your *right* hand can feel the warmness of your right thigh, warmth growing and spreading... from the wrist to the fingertips. The left hand remains stiff, but the right hand is getting warmer. *[Pause.]* Can you feel the warmth?

Patient: *[Nodding.]* **... Yes, I, guess so...** *[Pause.]*

[At this point, the patient's left hand still has catalepsy, but the other parts of the body are beginning to become more relaxed.]

Clinician: Good. Enjoy that sensation. *[Pause.]* Now, when the right hand becomes warm, you may also start to feel the warmth spreading out to the right arm... and the right leg. ... It may start slowly... but you may sense the flow of

warmth spreading... relaxing areas of the body that were stuck.

[Patient maintains silence, taking his time feeling the sensations. There seems to be no negative emotions.]

Clinician: How do you feel?

Patient: Hmm... A slow warmth. *[Pause.]* **Not tingling, but fluffy** *[Pause.]* **it's flowing...**

As the clinician continues with this procedure, the patient gradually feels the relaxing sensations spread. The patient also experiences a reduction in pain and a relaxed and pleasant mood. But because the catalepsy in the left hand remains, step three involves relaxing the catalepsy while in the hypnotic state.

Step Three: Relaxing the Catalepsy (and an Indirect Suggestion for Pain Management)

Clinician: Now that you are feeling quite relaxed, you can also notice that your left hand remains stiff, can't you?

Patient: *[Nods.]*

Clinician: And now, I would like to invite you to start to relax that stiff left hand. Would that be okay with you?

Patient: *[Nods.]*

Clinician: Okay... now take a deep breath.... That's right, very relaxing.... Where in your left hand do you think you should focus on to help you to let go of the tension? *[Pause.]*

Patient: Mmm... maybe at the base of my thumb? No... pinky finger? *[Trying one after another]* **If I try opening my index finger while I concentrate on the base of my thumb...** *[The catalepsy begins to dissipate.]*

Clinician: Good. You can relax the hand by yourself. Be sure to hold on to that sense of loosening...

Patient: Oh, it's getting loose and opening. *[Pause.]* It's starting to move... I can move it by myself...

Clinician: Good. That way you can naturally loosen that stiffness...

Patient: *[Nods.]*

Clinician: Now, the left arm and left leg are also relaxing... becoming more and more relaxed. ... Now take a deep, deep breath.... And this will help to spread the relaxing sensations in your left leg to your thigh... *[Pause.]* and your belly too. Warm and comfortable... *[Pause.]* Now, this warm sensation is easing the discomfort and the pain... a nice feeling...

Very good. ... This relaxed feeling will be stored in and remembered by your body; you do not have to consciously remember it. Whenever your body feels any tension or pain, the comfort and relaxation can spontaneously arise. ... You can experience the comfort... and you have already noticed that you can relax whenever you feel the stiffness yourself, and you can even produce that stiffness anytime it will be useful to you...

[Post-hypnotic suggestions continue.]

Here I have presented an example of the use of catalepsy while inducing hypnotic relaxation. The idea of using catalepsy here came from the patient's comment, "It's no good relaxing, I must stay focused at all times." This focusing of attention was the strategy the patient used to deal with his pain, although ultimately it interfered with his ability to "let go" and relax, which is an established strategy for pain management for many patients.

Instead of pushing forward with a technique that was clearly not going to be effective for this patient, I utilized an alternative induction (catalepsy), using as a cue the patient's own words. Ultimately, the patient was able to relax himself with, as he put it, "tension remaining in some part of the body," in the hypnotic state. This allowed him to also create and experience relaxing feelings (in other parts of the body), which ultimately resulted in more comfort. Moreover, the experience of being able to relax catalepsy on his own was effective in learning how to manage pain all by himself.

The word "settle down" (*mi o katameru*) is used as an idiom for getting married in Japan, although its direct meaning in Japanese is to "stiffen." The experience of controlling his own catalepsy was also indirectly teaching him how to "stiffen" (*mi o katameru*), which in this case was an indirect suggestion for a successful marriage.

This case illustrates the importance of using the patient's own words and metaphors to optimize the efficacy of the hypnotic suggestions. The patient's words provide important information for creating effective hypnotic suggestions, not only for the treatment of chronic pain, but also for the treatment of many other intractable chronic pain conditions.

In this case, the patient learning how to induce and then relax catalepsy was not only effective for pain reduction from a physiological point of view, it also effectively reduced his psychological suffering from his social situation (i.e., stressful work environment), which was contributing to his overall experience of pain. In addition, although each of the hypnotic sessions was targeting pain reduction on the surface, they also worked as indirect suggestions to help him solve the psychosocial issues he was facing.

References

Adachi, T., Fujino, H., Nakae, A., Mashimo, T., & Sasaki, J. (2014). A meta-analysis of hypnosis for chronic pain problem: A comparison between hypnosis, standard care, and other psychological interventions. *International Journal of Clinical and Experimental Hypnosis, 62*, 1-28.

Jensen, M. P., & Patterson D. R. (2006). Hypnotic treatment of chronic pain. *Journal of Behavioral Medicine, 29*, 95-124.

Jensen, M. P. (2016). Pain management: Chronic pain. In: G.R. Elkins (Ed.), *Handbook of medical and psychological hypnosis: Foundations, applications, and professional issues* (pp. 341-360). New York, NY: Springer.

Kandabashi, J. (2011). *Waza wo hagukumu – Seishin Igaku no Chi to Waza.* Tokyo, Japan: Nakayama Shoten.

Matsuki, S. (2005). *Learning from mistakes.* Presented at the Japanese Society of Clinical Hypnosis 2005 annual congress.

Matsuki, S. (2008). Hypnotherapy for personality disorder. *Japanese Journal of Clinical Psychology, 8*, 661-667.

Matsuki, S. (2012). Saimin ryouhou. In: T. Ibi (Ed.), *Shinri-Rinshou wo minaosu "Kaizai" Ryouhou -Taijin Enjyo no Atarashii Shiten* (pp. 141-153). Tokyo, Japan: Akashi Shoten.

Ogiso, K., Koriyama, N., Akao, A., Otsuji, M., Goto, T., Fujisaki, N., ... Matsuki, S. (2015). Type I diabetes complicated with uncontrollable adult cyclic vomiting syndrome: A case report. *Journal of Diabetes & Metabolic Disorders, 10*, 14-22.

Mizutani M. (2006). Hypnotically structured autogenic training applied to CRPS Type I patients. *Japanese Journal of Hypnosis, 49*, 7-19.

Mizutani, M. (2015a). Hypnotic self-control of chronic pain: An attempt to describe low back pain in a young man. *Japanese Journal of Hypnosis, 55,* 10-21.

Mizutani, M. (2015b). A need for a common set of descriptors for hypnosis in the treatment of pain: From a mail-survey conducted internationally. *Japanese Journal of Hypnosis, 55,* 10-21.

Whorwell, P., Prior, A., & Faragher, E. (1984). Controlled trial of hypnotherapy in the treatment of several refractory irritable-bowel syndrome. *Lancet, 324,* 1232-1234.

Whitehead, W. E. (2006). Hypnosis for irritable-bowel syndrome. The empirical evidence of therapeutic effects. *International Journal of Clinical and Experimental Hypnosis, 54,* 7-20.

For Further Reading

Matsuki, S. (in press). The Matsuki method: Therapists and clients working together to build a therapeutic "place" in trance. In M. P. Jensen (Ed.), *Handbook of hypnotic techniques, Volume 1.* Kirkland, WA: Denny Creek Press.

Matsuki, S. (2003). A study of the role of empathy played in hypnotherapy. *Japanese Journal of Hypnosis, 47,* 1-8.

Matsuki, S. (1991). Dealing with the content of "worry" and with the mode of handling "worry" in psychotherapy. *Journal of Japanese Clinical Psychology, 9,* 4-16.

CHAPTER 9

Transforming the Gestalt and Carrier of Chronic Pain: Two Hypnotherapeutic Approaches

Burkhard Peter

Burkhard Peter works as psychological psychotherapist in Munich, Germany. Having studied with Milton H. Erickson, he was the founding president of the Milton Erickson Society for Clinical Hypnosis Germany (MEG) (1978-1984). He has served as board member of the International Society of Hypnosis (1992-2000) and has organized several national and international hypnosis congresses (1984-2000). His publications focus mostly on hypnosis and hypnotherapy. He is Editor-in-Chief of the German journal Hypnose-ZHH, and serves on the editorial boards of several other hypnosis journals. He has been awarded a Fellowship from the American Society of Clinical Hypnosis (1997), the Lifetime Achievement Award from the Milton H. Erickson Foundation (1999), the Pierre Janet Award for Clinical Excellence from the International Society of Hypnosis (2004), and the Milton Erickson Award from the MEG (2006). He is also a lecturer of clinical hypnosis at the Ludwig-Maximilians-Universität München, Department of Clinical Psychology and Psychotherapy.

* * *

One of the fundamental ideas underlying hypnotherapy is that hypnosis can facilitate the construction of an *alternative reality*, during which therapeutic change is facilitated. The more real the experience feels to the patient, the more effectively the changes are transferred into the patient's everyday life (Peter, 2009a, 2015c). A further fundamental idea in modern hypnotherapy is the metaphor of the "unconscious mind," which is independent of the patient's rational and voluntary control and constitutes an integral part of the therapeutic process (Erickson & Rossi, 1977). The unconscious can be viewed as a resource with abilities and knowledge that are not consciously available to the patient prior to treatment (Peter, 2002; 2009b).

Both of these concepts are key to the two hypnotherapeutic approaches described in this chapter for chronic pain management: (1) the construction of a *pain-* or rather *symptom-gestalt* and (2) the creation of a *pain-* or rather *symptom-carrier*. Although both strategies can be conducted via guided imagery, irrespective of formal trance induction, they are more effective if conducted in hypnotic trance, given that the patient is sufficiently susceptible to hypnosis. This may be due to the fact that the psychophysiological flexibility of responsive patients is greater during a state of hypnotic trance (Crawford, 1989)—meaning that such patients are easier to guide while in trance as this enhances the "realness" of their experience; therefore making it more impactful (Kosslyn et al., 2000; Rainville et al., 1997).

Hypnotic Induction and Establishing Contact with the "Unconscious Mind"

A key aspect of hypnotherapy for chronic pain is the practice of self-hypnosis (Jensen, 2011). Self-hypnosis enables patients to independently repeat and deepen the strategies acquired during their therapy sessions. When teaching self-hypnosis, the induction should be kept simple so that patients can follow the steps easily. One example is the following sequence, which I use frequently: eye fixation, eyelid closure, staircase metaphor for deepening, and finally, establishing contact with the unconscious mind via arm levitation (see Peter, 2006, p. 39).

The first of the two strategies (cf. Peter, 2015a) described in this chapter is strictly symptom-oriented. Because of this, a preliminary consultation with the patient's unconscious mind via ideomotor signaling (Cheek, 1994; Peter, 2015d) might be indicated. After the initial trance induction, the unconscious should be asked whether a modification of the symptom is appropriate and reasonable, or whether there may be reasons for the symptom to remain. If permission is not granted, it would be preferable to address the underlying issue(s) first, using a problem-oriented strategy (see the second "symptom-carrier" technique, described in the latter half of this chapter). The first strategy, of modifying the symptom directly, is used only if the patient's unconscious mind explicitly grants permission for this modification.

Construction and Modification of a
Pain- or Symptom-Gestalt

Pain is a physical sensation that is often (but not always) the result of processing of stimulation from nociceptors in the body. As opposed to our remote senses (seeing and hearing), pain can be difficult to ignore or to diminish by means of distraction (e.g., looking away or covering our ears; see Peter, 2001). In addition, the experience of pain often triggers negative affect—the suffering component of pain—which is sometimes disproportionately high in relation to the actual somatosensory stimulation, especially in patients with chronic pain.

The primary goal of the approach described here—the pain- or symptom-gestalt technique—is to divert the perception of pain from the kinesthetic mode to sensory modalities that are more likely to enable the externalization of the symptom, thus facilitating a modification of the experience. These other modalities are primarily visual, acoustical, and tactile. The technique involves four steps.

The Four Steps of the Symptom-Gestalt Approach

Step 1: Identification and initial modification of the pain border. The basic idea of this technique is to first create an overall internal representation (gestalt) of the pain experience and then to modify this representation in order to alter the pain experience. It begins by asking the patient to, "Please tell me, exactly, *where* in your body do you feel the pain?"

Next, the *border* of pain needs to be determined. This indirectly suggests that pain-free areas exist and that the perception of pain can be controlled. Giving the patient an imaginary pencil or marker, the clinician can say,

Please outline the area of discomfort with the pencil/marker to indicate exactly where you hurt. This will tell us where the pain is (inside the border) and also where you are *pain free*. For some sections of the border, the line between the pain and pain-free areas may be very clear; in others, it could be blurry. Go ahead and draw the outline as accurately as possible.

The first direct transformation could then seek to modify the *border of pain*. Starting with a part of the border where the pain area extends *into* pain-free areas is often best, for changing this section of the border can be easier than shrinking the entire area. The clinician says,

Now, please find an appropriate spot on the border, a section where the border of pain can be changed; perhaps a spot where it can be changed most easily. You can pull the line in; bringing some of the pain-free area into the pain area. Or you might experiment and push the border out, expanding the area of pain into new areas.

Step 2: Changing to different sensory modalities. The following are questions that facilitate an exploration of the possibilities for changing pain perceptions into *different sensory modalities*:

Visual: Now, examine the pain within the border. What does it look like? Does it have a certain color? In what way does it look different from the pain-free area?

Auditory: Perhaps it is possible to listen to the pain. Not everybody can, but some people really are able to hear their pain. What would the pain sound like if you could hear it?

Tactile: You could also touch your pain with your fingers; how does it feel? What is its consistency? Is it firm or soft? What is the temperature? Is it warm or cool? Explore the surface texture. Is it rough, coarse, or smooth? Dry or damp?

During this exercise, the clinician should remember—or take notes about—the specific words the patient uses to describe the pain. This will enable the clinician to utilize the same words as the patient in the suggestions that follow. A simple way to memorize the patient's terminology is to apply a very basic form of reflective listening, the so-called "parrot" technique, which puts the patient in a "yes-set" (a mindful state of agreement). With this strategy, the therapist simply echoes the same nouns or adjectives the patient uses.

Patient: My pain is dark-red on the inside and becomes lighter towards the borderline.

Clinician: Ah, yes, dark-red on the inside and lighter towards the border. And how does it look beyond the border?

Finally, the clinician helps the patient modify the pain-gestalt that had been established. The best way to achieve this with respect to the perception of pain is to address its *sensory qualities*. At this point, the hypnotherapeutic approach starts to diverge from Cognitive Behavioral Therapy (CBT). In CBT, the patient is asked to actively and voluntarily modify each sensory quality (e.g., visual: "If you were to modify the bright red color of your pain, if you made it lighter or darker, or if you would paint it in a different color, what would that do?"; auditory: "If this loud hammering or drilling noise were to slowly dissipate, if you would listen to something else..."; tactile: "If you would take the pain into your hand, and pet it, shape it, or squeeze it..."). In hypnotherapy, however, the patient is invited to go even deeper into trance and to explicitly get in touch with his/her unconscious mind, authorizing it to automatically choose and implement the most appropriate modifications; this can be facilitated by two additional steps:

Step 3: Presenting the pain-gestalt to the unconscious. The clinician can now repeat the words the patient used previously in his/her description of the externalized pain-gestalt—starting with the area described by the border and continuing with the various modalities and qualities of the pain-gestalt. The patient is asked to present these modalities to his/her unconscious mind.

Now, allow yourself to go even deeper into trance, and contact your unconscious mind. Explain to the unconscious mind what we just talked about, telling it that the border of pain runs from here to there... and the area inside of the border has these colors... and if you listen carefully, you can hear from inside the border... *[etc.]*

Step 4: Inviting the unconscious to modify the pain-gestalt. At this point, the unconscious is invited to transform the pain-gestalt in a way that is helpful for the patient. The therapist facilitates this process by repeating all the words that the patient used to describe the pain, except now, the clinician provides specific suggestions for change. For example,

I am curious how... /I am sure that... your unconscious is starting to change the border. ... Be very mindful and pay close attention to how... your unconscious continues to change the border. ... And I wonder, how will it modify the color...? *[etc.]*

In this step, the unconscious is invited to actively, yet automatically, modify the different aspects of pain. The patient does not implement the changes himself/herself, but rather allows the unconscious mind to do this work. The role of the clinician is to provide an abundance of indirect and interspersed directions or suggestions for the modification to happen (Erickson, 1966).

Case Example Using the Pain Gestalt Technique

For many years, Mr. B had been suffering from left-sided facial pain. Different doctors and dentists had given Mr. B a variety of diagnoses, including nonspecific facial pain, temporomandibular joint dysfunction, and trigeminal neuralgia. Outside of hypnosis, Mr. B was able to draw a border indicating that the area of his pain included the upper part of his face (temple and his cheekbone) rather well; but the border became blurred in the lower area, close to his teeth. Near the temple, the color was a dark red. In pain-free areas, the color was beige. Down towards the jaw the color faded to a lighter red. Thus, his initial symptom-gestalt had visual characteristics; he was not able to describe or experience his pain as having auditory or tactile characteristics.

Still outside of hypnosis, I asked the patient to alter the border of the pain starting at any point, from the temporomandibular joint up to the hair line or back towards his ear, or from the temporomandibular joint towards the nose. When changing the borders, I asked him to also pay close attention to how this influenced the colors.

He was able to move the border towards his nose; and as he did so, the dark red became lighter towards the temple. He was also able to move the more "fuzzy" border on the bottom of the painful area towards the area underneath his lower jaw. At this point, he could no longer differentiate between areas that were painful and areas that were not painful, because the colors ended up blending; the rose color turned lighter and gave way to a beige color. This illustrates this patient's ability to modify his pain-gestalt by changing its localization and visual sensory qualities based on CBT.

Mr. B was able to practice this exercise at home and it reduced his pain by about half. The only challenge was that this was difficult for him and took a great deal of concentration. Moreover, his pain returned to its original intensity as soon as he stopped engaging in each exercise. At this point, I taught him self-hypnosis, which resulted in pain relief for the duration of trance during the therapy sessions as well as at home; however, the pain always returned as soon as the trance was over.

We then repeated the creation and modification of a pain-gestalt, this time while in hypnotic trance and with the explicit suggestions as follows:

Clinician: Now, you can entrust your unconscious or the "consciousness of your body" with making changes in your pain's border, in order to achieve *lasting pain relief*. Do not consciously control this process; leave everything to your unconscious, it knows best what you really need.

Then you can be curious, how... the colors are starting to change, the entire gestalt is starting to change, the border is thinning, it is becoming blurry, and pleasant warm colors are starting to blend in from the outside, the border is beginning to dissolve... more and more... so... even more delicate warm colors are pouring in from the outside, leaving the entire area soft... and comfortable... but leave everything to your unconscious, the consciousness of your body, because it knows best, what and how this will take place...

While his unconscious was implementing these changes, I suggested that his left hand lift by ideomotor force, all the way to his cheek. The hand was asked to remain there until all of the painful sensations dissolved. Afterwards, his hand was instructed to slowly move back down, at the pace that his unconscious needed to achieve pain relief that would remain, as he moved into his normal awareness. We essentially repeated the same exercise in several subsequent sessions;

audio recordings allowed him to conduct regular practice sessions at home.

As a result, the pain-free intervals lasted longer, and the intensity as well as quality of his pain continued to decrease. About six months and 25 sessions later, the patient said that the pain relief he had achieved was now satisfactory. At follow-up, six months after treatment, the benefits maintained.

Indications for and Contraindications of the Symptom-Gestalt Technique

Representing a primarily symptom-oriented approach, the strategy of pain- or rather symptom-gestalt is well-suited for clearly defined pain problems that have minimal psychological overlay. However, this approach is less useful for patients presenting with more diffuse pain, migratory pain, or multifocal pain problems. In principle, this technique does not require high hypnotizability or even a formal induction of hypnosis, although including a more formal hypnotic trance can enhance efficacy, as noted previously.

Nevertheless, this strategy requires the patient to be motivated and willing to participate actively. Also, a certain degree of imaginative capability is useful. This approach is not suited for patients who are effectively using a distraction strategy to cope with their pain. In this case, it could interfere with their preferred strategy, leading to an increased perception of pain, which, in turn, could undermine rapport and motivation.

Construction and Modification
of the Symptom Carrier

If the pain plays an important functional role for the patient, or if the pain is diffuse or migratory—all characteristics of psychosomatic or somatoform pain—it can be difficult to motivate the patient to construct and alter a pain- or symptom-gestalt. Patients presenting with somatoform pain problems are likely to dismiss the idea of a possible connection between their discomfort and their psychological history or personal circumstances; they often believe in a purely physical cause for their pain.

However, attributing a lack of insight to these patients is not necessarily justified. It remains possible that their symptoms were caused by a series of subliminal stressors that occurred outside of the patient's conscious perception. Therefore, the patient may not be aware of his/her pain's etiology and is justifiably denying any underlying psychological cause.

It is the clinician's responsibility to provide a coherent bio-psycho-social model for the etiology of pain; to familiarize the patient with the idea that the pain might not be strictly connected to a physical malfunction. The following approach, called *pain-* or rather *symptom-carrier* technique, is indicated for such patients. It has already been described for psychosomatic disorders by Meiss (2015) and it constitutes a special variant of the "representative technique" (Bongartz & Bongartz, 2015).

While the symptom-gestalt strategy, as described above, externalizes the symptom and the internal observer remains within the patient, the symptom-carrier strategy externalizes the internal observer. The patient is asked to watch the symptom- or pain-carrier from a distant place that is safe and comfortable. This makes it possible for the symptom-carrier to be observed in his/her entirety, enabling the patient to gain bigger-picture insight or information. However, these patients often lack the necessary self-reflection or readiness for self-reflection, which can result in resistance. Therefore, a specific three-step series of interventions needs to be implemented, as described below.

The Three Steps of the Symptom-Carrier Technique

Step 1: Construction of the Symptom-Carrier. Following trance induction, the patient is invited to imagine a person who is a complete stranger who neither resembles the patient or anybody the patient knows (this helps to make it less likely that the patient will get distracted by irrelevant details or resistance-evoking aspects of the image). The only thing the patient knows about this stranger is that he/she has the same symptoms as the patient.

The patient is then asked to describe this person by responding to the therapist's questions. The goal here is to make the experience as real as possible (Peter, 2001):

Clinician: Please let me know the perspective you see him/her from and the distance between you and that person.

It is very important in this early stage for the patient as the observer to keep a sufficient distance between himself/herself and the symptom-carrier, so the patient can remain emotionally neutral. Questions regarding the exact perspective ("Do you see that person from above or from the side? How far away is he/she?") help to enhance this perspective, as well as the sense of reality. The clinician can ask,

Can you describe the person's position? Is this person standing, sitting, or lying down? *[And in the event that the symptom-carrier is standing,]* **Is this person standing with both feet firmly on the ground? Is the person standing with the legs close together or far apart? Are both knees straight or is one leg supporting the other? ... Observe him/her in**

detail, how the legs are attached to the hips, if the hips are straight or tilted. ... Pay attention to how the back relates to the hips. Is the back completely straight or bent toward one side or the other? What is the position of the shoulders? Are they straight or hanging towards the front? ... Pay attention to the neck and how the head sits on the neck... is it bent forward or tilted back? ... Examine the facial expressions, the tension of the muscles around the mouth, eyes, and forehead.

And now imagine having X-ray vision, being able to see into that person's body and examine the muscle tone, the tendons, and the blood vessels. The organs in the chest, the capacity of the lungs and heart, and the organs in the abdomen, the intestines... [etc.]

Ideally (although this does not always happen right away), this anatomical-physiological discussion will facilitate the insight that, based on the symptom-carrier's posture and the condition of the internal organs, the development of the symptoms was inevitable.

To provide an example of the first step of the symptom-carrier technique, here I describe the case of a young women presenting with diffuse pain in her upper abdomen that had no clear biomedical basis described a pain-carrier who was a young and energetic female manager, walking briskly through a park toward her office. She walked in a bolt upright position. Her thoughts were focused on her work in the office; so much so that she was wearing blinders, completely oblivious to her immediate surroundings. She was very athletic. Her entire musculoskeletal system was in perfect shape, as was her cardiovascular system.

The patient became irritated in response to my request for her to describe the area between chest and pelvis of the manager, because she was not able to see anything in the manager's abdominal area. In fact, it appeared as a gaping hole, as if this woman was missing her abdomen altogether. Accordingly, the patient was unable to explain how the manger nourishes herself, nor how she perceives hunger and satiation; neither of these were of any importance to this woman. In her view, eating was mostly a waste of time. She reluctantly ate only every now and then, just to get it over with.

I did not comment on this and simply asked if there was anything else worth mentioning that I had not inquired about up to that point. After the patient said there was nothing else to describe, I then moved on to the next step; the construction of the "anti-symptom-carrier."

Step 2: Construction of the Anti-Symptom-Carrier. The anti-symptom-carrier is the exact opposite of the symptom-carrier. For some patients, this requires a more detailed explanation, as they tend to interpret the anti-symptom-carrier as a representation of the symptom-carrier (or rather themselves) *after* full recovery. But the anti-symptom-carrier should be an entirely different person. Below are the instructions I usually provide to patients:

Again, picture somebody you don't know, all you know about that person is that he or she has *never, ever,* suffered from pain like yours. He or she is resilient; built in a way that he or she could *never* experience your discomfort. This person's way of life, his/her attitude towards life, his/her unique experiences, preclude him/her from ever experiencing your pain...

The anti-symptom-carrier is created by using the same anatomical-physiological questions that are used to create the symptom-carrier, as described previously. Ideally, this leads the patient to the insight that this person's physical constitution prevents him/her from ever developing this sort of pain.

The patient with upper abdominal pain, introduced previously, spontaneously visualized her anti-symptom-carrier to be a woman. This woman was sprawling on a chaise longue, with no obligations. She was obviously enjoying herself. Further descriptions revealed that this woman's body was nowhere close to being as firm as the symptom-carrier's; it was *not* athletically built. It had soft muscles and soft skin. She was even slightly chubby, and her olfactory and gustatory senses were very pronounced.

Apparently, she valued delicious food as well as all the other pleasantries that life has to offer for physical well-being. She felt very comfortable, particularly in her body. All her senses, including hearing, smell, and sense of touch, seemed to be directed towards pleasurable experiences. The only disadvantage for this woman—from my patient's point of view—was that she obviously did not have any professional aspirations, nor any interest in changing her situation.

During the construction of the anti-symptom-carrier, two things are of major importance: (1) a sufficiently deep state of trance on the part of the patient (which enhances the patient's cognitive tolerance for the unfamiliar) and (2) keeping the inquiry neutral by abstaining from any judgment or interpretation of meaning. Matter-of-fact questions regarding the person's physiological and anatomical condition help to prevent resistance.

Premature identification of the patient with either one of the representative figures should be avoided, as this can easily result in resisting/opposing reactions. During the construction of the anti-symptom-carrier, distorted cartoon-like anti-types may surface. They may be appalling to the patient, leading to their rejection and possibly even causing the patient to discontinue any further participation (e.g., a patient saying, "I have nothing in common with someone like that. Do you think, in order to overcome my pain, I have to become as repulsive as this person?").

Hypnotherapists approaching the patient from an Ericksonian tradition usually avoid any direct interpretation of images presented by the patient. They trust that the patient will be able to deduce the meaning independently as soon as he/she is ready. Or rather, insight will occur once the patient is prepared not only to understand the meaning cognitively, but to embrace it emotionally. This insight will then be reflected by an adaptive change. To ensure that insight occurs only when the patient is ready, the therapist may even attempt to actively suppress a premature comprehension of meaningful insight, using so-called "amnesia techniques" (Peter, 2015b).

Step 3: Consolidation of Symptom-Carrier and Anti-Symptom-Carrier. After the two opposing representations have been constructed, it is now time for them to approach one another. They need to get close enough to be able to understand the other person's point of view. In doing so, the primary goal is not necessarily their integration, although this need not be inhibited should it occur spontaneously. The goal is merely for each of them to understand what it is like to be the other person and how their lifestyles as well as their attitudes towards life are affected by the pain or—vice versa—being pain free. This part of treatment usually takes a number of sessions, since adaptive processes can take time. Although the clinician should facilitate and attend to these processes, the clinician should not substantially influence or guide them.

In trance, the patient is asked to watch the symptom-carrier walk towards the anti-symptom-carrier until he or she is standing behind the anti-symptom-carrier. The symptom-carrier should then look over the shoulders of the anti-symptom-carrier in order to see the world from the other person's point of view; virtually seeing it from his/her perspective, listening to the noises (or voices) that can be heard from his/her perspective, and learning how the anti-symptom-carrier experiences his/her environment and life. If useful, other sensory modalities, such as olfactory or gustatory may be implemented as well.

Eventually, the symptom-carrier is asked to stretch out his/her hand and touch the anti-symptom-carrier on the back or shoulder. Then, the symptom-carrier allows the anti-symptom-carrier's emotional state and physiological feelings to gradually flow over and into the symptom-carrier. In the event that this becomes overwhelming, or if some sort of discomfort arises, the symptom-carrier can let go. Allowing the patient to discontinue the exercise in this way is crucial for the patient's sense of safety; the patient should not be expected to have to deal with somebody else's feelings if he/she does not want to or is not ready to.

Afterwards, the anti-symptom-carrier is asked to walk towards the symptom-carrier, stand behind the symptom-carrier, and to follow the same procedure as the symptom-carrier did. This process gives both representatives the opportunity to experience a different point of view and to adapt to those parts of the different view that they find most useful.

The aspect of this technique that is explicitly hypnotic—beyond the state of hypnotic trance—is that every now and then the patient's unconscious mind is invited to attend to and comment on the process. It is invited to consider either a newly gained view or the situation as a whole, sometimes to explicitly investigate further if a strong defensive reaction occurs.

So, continuing with the case report, the patient with upper abdominal pain, mentioned above, initially refused to lay down next to the chubby, lascivious, and "useless" person on the chaise longue, arguing that the anti-symptom-carrier was too far removed from her own world.

Therefore, I asked the anti-symptom-carrier to approach and walk behind the symptom-carrier who was hastily rushing through the park. Even though she made an attempt to do so, it only took a short while before it became clear that the anti-symptom-carrier was unable to keep up with the symptom-carrier. Soon, she was out of breath and started to feel sick to her stomach; it was early morning (much earlier than she usually awakens), and she had not had breakfast yet. She lost contact with the symptom-carrier and was surprised at how the other woman was able to already have her mind on her office work and to be planning her day, despite her pain.

I suggested that she ask the symptom-carrier if she would consider slowing down for her and whether she would be willing to share some of her thoughts. This suggestion yielded a positive reaction; the symptom-carrier slowed down, seemed surprised by the fact that somebody was interested in her thoughts and willingly answered all kinds of questions.

In doing so, I assisted the anti-symptom-carrier by suggesting further questions, such as, "How do you do that—to disregard your empty stomach? Yours has to be in the same discomfort as mine." The response, "Right now, I have other things to do than to think about my stomach!" was incomprehensible for the anti-symptom-carrier, because she could only feel mentally fit if her body felt good as well. The anti-symptom-carrier was unable to separate her body and mind, which is why she always had to tend to her body before she could consider doing or thinking about anything else, much less anything of importance.

At this point, I explained that people differ in many ways and that one of those ways is by how well they can dissociate from their body and its perceptions. Being able to dissociate in this way can have advantages, because for such individuals the body's sensations can be put aside until tasks have been completed.

But dissociation can also have disadvantages. If certain physical signals—such as a light hunger or an empty stomach—are no longer perceived, the appropriate action needed to address one's physical needs can be impeded. Over time, this can result in serious symptoms, such as pain. Thus, while the initial discomfort is minor, it is possible to ignore and can go unnoticed, until the pain forcefully enters consciousness. Unfortunately, by then, it usually has turned into a serious symptom that can no longer be ignored.

It took a number of sessions for the symptom-carrier to be willing to enter the world of the anti-symptom-carrier. The unconscious indicated that the patient was ready by levitating the "yes-hand" in response to one of my repeated questions about this readiness. According to a previous agreement, the patient began by using her visual modality only and looked around the other woman's room. Many things seemed strange to her, but she ended up liking some of the things she saw. I later learned that she had started to implement minor modifications in her own apartment during this time.

Next, she was ready to explore the anti-symptom-carrier's olfactory and tactile modalities; she tried out different fragrances and bath essences. She subsequently moved on to the gustatory modality. It was only after this that she started to detect a vague and cautious sensation in her abdomen.

At first, this triggered discomfort and even pain, leading to spontaneous age regressions, which we utilized to work through several negative experiences in her childhood and early adolescence. This constituted the problem-oriented part of the treatment and took a significant number of sessions to address. The patient had been abused physically through repeated beatings, mostly from her father. During one of these beatings when she was a child, she discovered that she could dissociate from her body, which enabled her to no longer feel the pain.

She took advantage of this ability, and at some point, even started to provoke her father by challenging him to beat her. This, in turn, resulted in ongoing reinforcement of her ability to dissociate. Over the course of this trauma-oriented therapy, the patient's upper abdominal pain finally started to dissipate.

Conclusion

The pain-carrier strategy aims to help the patient keep a sufficient distance from the problem, in order to allow him/her to view the symptoms from a new perspective. This facilitates the patient being able to develop insight into the etiology and role of the presenting symptom or dysfunction. In general, the state of hypnotic trance facilitates the dissociation from affect, as well as facilitating imagination. The metaphorical instance of the unconscious enables a prolonged tolerance for cognitive dissonances; it increases the tolerance of cognitive and emotional perspectives that may seem foreign, embarrassing, or antagonistic to the conscious mind, and which are therefore usually avoided.

Indications for and Contraindications of the Symptom-Carrier Technique

Although symbolic strategies require neither formal hypnosis nor high hypnotizability, a certain level of imaginative capability is indispensable. These strategies are well-suited for problem-oriented approaches that address psychosomatic or somatoform symptoms. Particularly for the latter, a certain willingness or capability for insight is required; otherwise the approaches might be dismissed as mere "psycho games."

References

Bongartz, B., & Bongartz, W. (2015). Stellvertretertechnik. In D. Revenstorf & B. Peter (Eds.), *Hypnose in Psychotherapie, Psychosomatik und Medizin. Ein Manual für die Praxis* (2nd ed., pp. 265-272). Heidelberg, Germany: Springer.

Cheek, D. B. (1994). *Hypnosis. The applicaton of ideomotor techniques*. Boston, MA: Allyn and Bacon.

Crawford, H. J. (1989). Cognitive and physiological flexibility: Multiple pathways to hypnotic responsiveness. In V. A. Gheorghiu, P. Netter, H. J. Eysenck, & R. Rosenthal (Eds.), *Suggestion and suggestibility: Theory and research* (pp. 155-168). Heidelberg, Germany: Springer.

Erickson, M. H. (1966). The interspersal hypnotic technique for symptom correction and pain control. *American Journal of Clinical Hypnosis, 8,* 198-209.

Erickson, M. H., & Rossi, E. L. (1977). Autohypnotic experiences of Milton H. Erickson. *American Journal of Clinical Hypnosis, 20*(1), 36-54.

Jensen, M. P. (2011). *Hypnosis for chronic pain management: Therapist guide.* Oxford, United Kingdom: Oxford University Press.

Kosslyn, S. M., Thompson, W. L., Constantini-Ferrando, M. F., Alpert, N. M., & Spiegel, D. (2000). Hypnotic visual illusion alters color processing in the brain. *American Journal of Psychiatry, 157,* 1270-1284.

Meiss, O. (2015). Psychosomatische Störungen. In D. Revenstorf & B. Peter (Eds.), *Hypnose in Psychotherapie, Psychosomatik und Medizin. Ein Manual für die Praxis* (3rd ed., pp. 541-550). Heidelberg, Germany: Springer.

Peter, B. (2001). Construction of reality and hypnotic phenomena. *Hypnosis International Monographs, 5,* 103-112.

Peter, B. (2002). The "therapeutic tertium": On the use and usefulness of an old metaphor. *Hypnosis International Monographs, 6,* 247-258.

Peter, B. (2006). *Einführung in die Hypnotherapie.* Heidelberg, Germany: Carl Auer.

Peter, B. (2009a). Is it useful to induce a hypnotic trance? A hypnotherapist's view on recent neuroimaging results. *Contemporary Hypnosis, 26,* 132-145.

Peter, B. (2009b). Zur Ideengeschichte des Unbewussten in Hypnose und Psychoanalyse. *Hypnose-ZHH, 4,* 49-78.

Peter, B. (2015a). Chronische Schmerzen. In D. Revenstorf & B. Peter (Eds.), *Hypnose in Psychotherapie, Psychosomatik und Medizin: Ein Manual für die Praxis* (3rd ed., pp. 593-605). Heidelberg, Germany: Springer.

Peter, B. (2015b). Hypermnesie und Amnesie. In D. Revenstorf & B. Peter (Eds.), *Hypnose in Psychotherapie, Psychosomatik und Medizin. Ein Manual für die Praxis* (3rd ed., pp. 273-283). Heidelberg, Germany: Springer.

Peter, B. (2015c). Hypnosis. In J. D. Wright (Ed.), *International Encyclopedia of the Social & Behavioral Sciences (2ⁿᵈ ed)* (pp. 458-464). Oxford, United Kinfdom: Elsevier.

Peter, B. (2015d). Ideomotorische Hypnoserituale. In D. Revenstorf & B. Peter (Eds.), *Hypnose in Psychotherapie, Psychosomatik und Medizin. Ein Manual für die Praxis* (3 ʳᵈ ed., pp. 175-185). Heidelberg, Germany: Springer.

Rainville, P., Duncan, G. H., Price, D. D., Carrier, B., & Bushnell, M. C. (1997). Pain affect encoded in human anterior cingulate but not somatosensory cortex. *Science, 277*, 968-971.

CHAPTER 10

Hypnotic Approaches Used by Milton Erickson for the Treatment of Chronic Pain

Roxanna Erickson-Klein

Roxanna Erickson-Klein is the daughter of Milton H. Erickson, who was broadly known for his development of hypnosis as a powerful medical resource, and who worked extensively with patients with chronic pain. His own experiences with severe poliomyelitis and subsequent post-polio syndrome provided a forum to put his ideas to the test. At a very early age, Roxanna, one of Erickson's eight children, became fascinated with the psychosocial and hypnotic strategies Erickson used for pain management. One of Erickson's dedications to her calls her "the greeter of my patients," reinforcing her own interest and sensitivity. She learned experientially how to approach others who suffer and to offer ideas and hope that seemed to make a difference. Her career choice as a registered nurse led her to work with individuals in a variety of settings, including home hospice for those with terminal conditions. In many ways, acute crises and natural life decline are easier to work with than helping individuals whose chronic pain and confusing journey through medical resources have depleted their hope. While Roxanna maintains her nursing license, her current professional focus is in professional counseling and teaching the value of hypnosis, especially for conditions that have a strong physiological component. An advocate of primary materials, she has worked with Ernest and Kathryn Rossi to edit and to make available the Collected Works of Milton H. Erickson (Rossi et al., 2008a, 2008b, 2008c, 2008d, 2009, 2010a, 2010b, 2010c, 2010d, 2010e, 2014a, 2014b, 2014c, 2014d, 2014e, 2015a, 2015b). In addition, she has written numerous chapters and articles. She teaches both locally and internationally and is dedicated to helping others extend their own repertoire of skills to serve those in need.

*   *   *

Milton H. Erickson is internationally recognized as the father of modern clinical hypnosis. He was among the many clinicians who ushered in hypnosis as a legitimate biomedical intervention, thus removing the mysterious shroud that had previously impaired its acceptance. Erickson's psychiatric career spanned from the 1920s through 1980. Throughout this time, he maintained a deep commitment to study, explore, and teach ways that hypnosis can promote healing both psychologically and physically.

While his own genius was an asset to his work, it created an ambiance of miraculous capabilities that he vehemently denied. He attested that all hypnosis is based on sound scientific foundations; measurable, learnable, and replicable. At the same time, he emphasized that what makes his work so powerful is its adaptability to the situation, the moment, and the individuals involved.

Early in my own life, I developed an intense interest in pain management. As Erickson's daughter, I was fortunate to have opportunities to discover the many ways that hypnosis can mitigate pain. My father recognized my interest and capitalized on countless occasions to foster my learning from the patients themselves. At the time of his death, when I was

30 years old, I was very skilled in both self- and hetero-hypnosis, and I was well established in my nursing career. I had additionally benefited from living at home during my college years, a time that coincided with the peak of my father's home-office teaching seminars. This rich learning opportunity included questions posed to him by the many people who came to learn from him.

Erickson promoted a process of self-discovery, growing self-awareness, and evolving transformative change that occurs below conscious awareness. The work he did created bonds that led to meaningful and lasting relationships with both his colleagues and his patients. That example gave me a sense of freedom to maintain contact with my own patients long after they completed treatment. Through communication, sometimes years after work is done, we are better able to appreciate how suggestions, post-hypnotic suggestions, and expectations for ongoing, healthy adaptation are expressed over time.

Erickson was strong in his stance that hypnosis is an adjunct to the treatment of pain, emphasizing that pain relief through hypnosis should never be undertaken as an alternative to more comprehensive medical care. An integral part of caretaking one's body involves pursuing "proper" diagnosis and treatment by scientifically trained members of the health care team. All effective treatments, including medication and/or surgical interventions when indicated, are part of the holistic approach that he advocated.

The current climate for treatment of chronic pain is decidedly different than it was decades ago. Erickson practiced in an era prior to distinctions and nuances we now recognize: chronic pain is different from acute pain, nerve pain is different from bone pain, slow pain is distinct from fast pain, and ongoing pain can bring about hypersensitivity. The important discoveries of today also bring a growing awareness of potentially disabling side-effects of well-intended treatments. As a clinician who sought to enhance symptom reduction and healing from within, Erickson's approaches remain current today. His ideas and creative approaches are relevant even after decades that witnessed the development of new treatment protocols, pharmaceutical advancements, and a greater understanding of pain physiology.

In April 1965, Erickson presented at the International Congress for Hypnosis and Psychosomatic Medicine in Paris. His talk: "An Introduction to the Study and Application of Hypnosis for Pain Control" has subsequently been reprinted a number of times and is further discussed in the *Collected Works of Milton H. Erickson* (Rossi et al., 2010c, pp. 95-104). At this historic 1965 meeting, he introduced 11 techniques for the treatment of pain that include: hypnotic direct and permissive indirect suggestions, amnesia, analgesia, anesthesia, replacement or substitution of sensations, displacement, dissociation, reinterpretation, time distortion, and diminution of pain.

In 1990, a quarter century later, I reviewed those techniques and re-classified them into five categories that could be flexibly used to evoke adaptive responses to the sensations patients experienced (Erickson-Klein, 1990). Though I have a strong commitment to use primary sources of information, a central aspect of the Ericksonian orientation is to absorb information, evaluate that information in the time and context of one's own life experience, and to adapt the selected approach to best suit the needs of the situation (Short, 2017). While Erickson's own works are replete with case discussions, few of those cases offer the detail, rationale, or explanations sought by professional audiences. What I offer in this chapter is a combination of Erickson's own words and techniques overlaid with my own observations and comments.

In working with a patient, a professional must have sufficient background to assess whether the sensations a patient experiences are worrisome, are indicative of a larger constellation of ongoing pathology, or are merely residual wounds that no longer contribute to the healing process.

Hypnotically, a starting point is often right there—right at the moment of awareness of sensation, right at the complaint that the patient presents with. "What is felt?" becomes an entry point of significance—not necessarily how, why, or how long, but merely "what." Careful attention must be given to the patient's own words, descriptive nouns, adjectives, gestures, correlates, and associations. I call this step, "Inviting the patient to tell their story." The reciprocal action of providing a listening ear for what is personally meaningful to the teller of the story is an important part of this initial step. Erickson describes this process:

> One need only to ask the patient to describe his pain and hear it variously described as dull, heavy, dragging, sharp, cutting, twisting, burning, nagging, stabbing, lancinating, biting, cold, hard, grinding, throbbing, gnawing, and a wealth of other such adjectival terms. These various descriptive interpretations of the pain experience are of marked importance in the hypnotic approach to the patient. (Rossi et al., 2010c, pp. 97-98)

I have developed a personal style to encourage expression by reflecting "key words" as a means of verifying that: I do hear, I am interested, and I seek to understand to the best of my ability. Often, in this most important conversational phase, patients reveal a reluctance to express themselves. The reticence may have to do with a history of avoidance or rejection by other listeners; at times it is related to a deep desire not to bring others down with them, or sometimes the patients themselves do not have the internal experience of putting words to their feelings. Whatever information I gather serves as a platform for the suggestions I offer as the patient becomes receptive to suggestion.

Further, as the patient begins to express him- or herself freely, a tendency to use visual, auditory, and kinesthetic words is revealed. I gather information about the patient's perspective on the meaning of discomfort, the passage of time, the positions of their body, the potency of symptoms, the margins of discomfort, constancy, what has been successful, the role of distraction, and the ability of the patient to capitalize on moments when the pain is less fearsome. I also ask direct, future-oriented questions about how the patient will notice change, what will become possible, and what joys await that are now beyond reach.

In this conversation, I adopt a frank, fact-finding demeanor, and when possible and appropriate, I bring a bit of humor or lightheartedness to the conversation. Through my own highly focused attention and the stimulation of mirror neurons, I bring awareness of the significance of what the patient expresses. I become a role model for dual attention to difficult conversation concurrent with the creation of a new, interesting relationship with a valued person. Once both the patient and I begin to express the possibility for comfort in the future, our conversation becomes a dance of tender hope and gentle movement that gives birth to potential.

Erickson's patients frequently reflected back on their own experiences with him during which an important change occurred. They often remarked about the paradox of certainty that change had occurred shrouded with the uncertainty of what exactly had taken place. Erickson frequently used indirect methods, talking about others who had come in just as miserable as the patient currently felt, while allowing the patient to find his or her own way into trance.

The omission of a formal trance induction was common. One patient described his experience thus: "The thing that impressed me the most, the secret to the Doctor- his secret- he sits here and I come in feeling sometimes just miserable, you know. I tell him how I'm feeling, and he sits there for a few minutes, and taking my case in relation to an anecdote, happening, things that have happened to other patients, and things that have happened to his friends, to his family, to himself" (Haley, 1985, p. 317). This particular patient had suffered from phantom limb pain and initially could not envision a future or even a present that included any semblance of comfort. He humorously went on to describe how his awareness shifted. "You know, he winds them all up together, and the first thing you know, lo and behold, I find out he's talking about me all the time" (Haley, 1985, p. 317).

In the same discussion, the patient described to Haley, "You know, my brother wrote and asked me if Dr. Erickson put me in a trance. I said 'No.' I said, 'the answer is yes and no.' I said but if you want the truth to the matter, Dr. Erickson puts himself in a trance. ... The first thing you know I'm in there with him" (Haley, 1985, pp. 317).

I recall that patient well. Early in the treatment, my father had asked me to demonstrate entering into a trance state and used my skills to illustrate a number of hypnotic phenomena.

I remember the patient's transformation from being withdrawn and suffering to becoming an active participant in life. The gentleman gave us a gift of shelled walnuts he had prepared as evidence that he could now do things he had previously left behind. At my father's suggestion, I decorated my wedding cake with this beautiful gift.

The interactive give and take of an initial session sets a tone for the evolution of future sessions. Relationship building at this stage calls for collaborative effort and a transparent honesty; a promise to do the best that each can despite a difficult and trying situation. Resources of the therapist can lend needed strengths to the patient; if the patient is reluctant to express hope, I call forth my own recollections of past successes. If a patient has little faith, I call forth my own faith in natural healing tendencies. On the other hand, if a patient demands a miracle, I reveal my own doubts. It is important to me that realistic possibilities be identified, or at least seeded, yet it is also important to navigate in a manner to avoid a sense of unfulfilled promises.

While I bring skills and experiences to the bedside (or chair-side), the patient is the one who is the true authority on what needs there are and whether desired progress is being made over time. In reinforcing these roles, I seek to engage the patient as an active participant. Engagement is essential and is often under-appreciated in the ambiance of the medical model which so often considers patients as passive recipients.

As the relationship is formed, various tools and techniques come into play. Erickson states that,

> Hypnosis is a state of awareness in which you offer communication with understandings and ideas to a patient and then you let them use those ideas and understandings in accord with their own unique

repertory of body learnings, their physiological learnings. (Rossi et al., 2010b, p. 316)

No single technique is likely to be totally successful in adapting to the complex and confusing signals that a patient senses. I begin with the strengths the patient identifies. I then proceed to work with the patient in a sequential, systematic way that offers opportunities for engagement of the patient's internal resources.

Erickson describes one case in which he used a series of techniques with a patient who suffered from terminal metastatic cancer. The techniques used in this case include: time distortion, transformation from a dull throbbing ache to fatigue and heaviness, dissociation, amnesia for past or future pain, and hypnotic analgesia and anesthesia. The patient withheld his own narcotics for 12 hours prior to meeting with Erickson in order to minimize interference with trance development. The next few pages offer a case discussion in which Erickson describes in detail his work with a patient.

> At the first hypnotic session all suggestions were directed to the induction of a state of profound physical fatigue, of overwhelming sleepiness, and of a need to enter physiological sleep and to rest sufficiently to permit the induction of a hypnotic trance. A light trance was induced that almost immediately lapsed into a physiological sleep of about 30 minutes' duration. He aroused from this definitely rested and most firmly convinced of the efficacy of hypnosis.
>
> A second and, this time, medium trance was then induced. Systematically a series of suggestions was given in which a direct use was made of the patient's actual symptomatology. The rationale for this was to

validate the hypnotic suggestions through utilization of the experiential validity of his symptoms.

Thus the patient was told that his body would feel tremendously heavy, that it would feel like a dull, leaden weight, so heavy that it would feel as if sodden with sleep and incapable of sensing anything else except heavy tiredness. These suggestions, repetitiously given and in varying phraseology to ensure comprehensive acceptance, were intended to utilize the patient's feeling of distressing weakness, previously unacceptable to him and to combine it with the complaint of "constant, heavy, dull, throbbing ache." In addition, suggestions were given that, again and again as he experienced the "dull, heavy tiredness" of his body, it would periodically go to sleep, while his mind remained awake.

Thus his distressing feeling of weakness and his dull, throbbing ache were utilized to secure a redirection and a reorientation of his attentiveness and responsiveness to his somatic sensations and to secure a new and acceptable perception of them. Also, by suggesting a sleeping of the body and wakefulness of the mind, a state of dissociation was induced.

The next step was to reorient and redirect his attentiveness and responsiveness to the sharp, brief, constantly recurring, agonizing pains from which he suffered, usually less than 10 minutes apart. These pains, while brief, less than one minute in duration as timed by a watch, were experienced by the patient subjectively as "endless" and as essentially "continuous" in character. (Rossi et al., 2010c, pp. 119-120)

Erickson then goes on to describe the steps he used to produce analgesia with this patient.

First of all, he was oriented in relationship to subjective time values by asking him, at the expiration of a sharp pain, to fix his attention rigidly on the movement of the minute hand of a clock and to await the next sharp pain. The slightly more than seven minutes of waiting in anticipatory dread seemed hours long to the patient, and it was with definite relief from his feeling of wretched expectation that he suffered the next sharp pain. Thus anticipation and pain, as separate experiences, were differentiated for him. ...

Next a careful explanation was given to him that freedom from the experience of pain could be accomplished in several ways—by anesthesia and by analgesia, both of which he understood, and by amnesia, which he did not understand. The explanation was offered that in amnesia for pain one could experience pain throughout its duration, but that one would immediately forget it and thus would not look back upon the experience with a feeling of horror and distress, nor look forward to another similar pain experience with anticipatory dread fear. In other words, each recurrent sharp pain could be and would become a totally unexpected and completely transient experience. Because it would be neither anticipated nor remembered, it would seem experientially to have no temporal duration. Hence, it would be experienced only as a momentary flash of sensation of such short duration that there would be no opportunity to recognize its character. In this fashion the patient was taught another aspect of time distortion—namely, a shortening, contraction, or condensation of subjective time. Thus, in addition to the possible hypnotic anesthesia, analgesia, or amnesia for the pains, there was also the hypnotic reduction of their subjective temporal duration which, in itself, would serve to diminish greatly the pain experience for the patient.

When these matters had been made clear to him, he was urged most insistently to employ all of the mechanisms that had been suggested—alteration of body sensations, body disorientation, dissociation, anesthesia, analgesia, amnesia, and subjective time condensation. In this way, it was argued, he could quite conceivably free himself from pain more readily than by employing a single psychological process. In addition, the suggestion was also offered emphatically that he employ subjective time expansion to lengthen experientially all periods of physical comfort, rest, or freedom from pain.

By this variety of differently directed suggestions, repetitiously given and in different phrasings to ensure adequate comprehension and acceptance, the patient's sharp recurring pains were abolished in large part insofar as observation of his objective behavior and his own subjective reports were concerned. However, it was noted that periodically he would lapse into a brief unresponsive stupor-like state of 10 to 50 seconds' duration, an item of behavior suggestive of a massive obscuring reaction to pain. It was noted that these were less frequent and shorter in duration than the original sharp pains had been. It was also observed that the patient appeared to have no realization whatsoever of his periodic lapses of awareness.

No systematic inquiry could be conducted into the actual efficacy of the suggestions. The patient simply reported that hypnosis had freed him almost completely of his pains, that he felt heavy, weak, and dull physically, and that not over twice a day did any pain "break through."

His general behavior with his family and friends validated his report. Some weeks after the beginning of hypnotic therapy the patient lapsed suddenly into coma and died without recovering consciousness. (Rossi et al., 2010c, pp. 120-121)

Erickson's practice setting and his own passion to work with complex cases afforded the opportunity for him to work extended hours—a reality that is not common in most of today's practice settings. While I have worked with complex cases such as the one described, it is now far more common in my private practice to encounter individuals who have limited injuries and have been unsatisfied with the status of their daily quality of life. To complement the case described by Erickson, I present one of my own, in which the concerns and responses are representative of many of those that I have seen.

Joe T. (his name has been changed here to ensure confidentiality) is a 77-year-old man who had been successfully treated a decade earlier by a lay hypnotist for chronic pain related to a back injury. Joe was committed to not taking pain medications—subsequent to his hypnosis intervention he had adapted productively to the limitations of his injury and considered himself to be as healthy and mobile as he thought reasonable. He sought a "tune up" with hypnosis to help him adapt to the changes associated with the natural aging process, which had compromised his ability to enjoy life.

I saw Joe a total of five visits, 60 minutes each time. My initial questions assured me that he was under the care of a physician and that the physician was aware of his old injury as well as the reports of increasing pain. I expressed great interest regarding the earlier successful hypnosis sessions and I questioned why he had not returned to that hypnotist. The original hypnotist was no longer in practice.

I then expressed intense curiosity regarding what the patient recalled of the initial successful hypnosis sessions. The intention of this was two-fold, my own interest in learning what worked so well that it held his pain at bay for a decade, but more importantly, to bring forth revivification of the potent effects through remembrance of trance. Interestingly, all Joe remembered consciously was a series of progressive relaxation exercises. He was aware that his own efforts to re-create those exercises had not successfully brought forth the sense of well-being found in his earlier experiences with the hypnotist. I assured him that amnesia is often an indicator of a deep trance response and emphasized that even if his conscious mind did not remember, his unconscious mind still held those lessons within. I accepted his case with the understanding that I wanted to teach him to find his own way into self-hypnosis so that he could adapt and make adjustments as he continued to age.

I reassured him that his past success was a strong indicator of future success and expressed uncertainty whether or not he would be consciously aware of "how" he found his way to comfort. I emphasized that the measure of success is beyond the feelings of the moment; rather, it is evaluated by his activity level and sense of well-being over a period of weeks.

Due to his history, I felt it was important to maintain the "magical" impression he came in with, even as I taught him that he could find his own pathway to activating unconscious resources. I encouraged him to use a formal ceremonial trance induction even when he set aside 20 minutes for a self-hypnosis practice session.

The first session focused on information, expectations, and goal setting. As part of the preparation for formal trance induction, I praised his previous responsiveness, giving him credit for being receptive, ready, and responsive to the signals his body had communicated. I also recognized his commitment to be conservative with medications, and I opined that situations can change, so total abstinence from medication was not necessarily an essential goal. I inquired whether he had preferences for imagery, and I attended carefully to his words that revealed that the times of discomfort were related to rising from a chair and to general aches that increased over the hours of the day.

In response to his expressions of anticipatory loss with his increasing age, I encouraged him to "take care of your body as if you will live to be 110." While he laughed at this prospect, it gave us a "reasonable" frame of reference for open discussion about natural decline and inevitable losses. Together we agreed that his ability to maintain a sense of "balanced energy" throughout the day would indicate that he was responding successfully to hypnosis. He added that he would like to rise comfortably from a seated position, and I added the expectation that he would find himself comfortable with setting aside a few 20-minute self-hypnosis practice sessions. We agreed that four to six sessions was a reasonable goal to expect positive progress and that he himself would judge how many sessions he would like to have.

In the second session, a ceremonial trance induction was offered and the trance work lasted for 40 minutes. He proved to be a ready subject, cooperative, and showing trance responsiveness through his immobility, slowed breathing, and generally peaceful appearance. While some clinicians work best with an interactive model, I prefer to offer suggestive monologue from which the patient can make selections and can choose what to attend to. Each subsequent session with him involved a "10-minute check-in" followed by an approximately 30-minute trance, with a bit of cognitive work at the conclusion.

I often begin with a formal induction routine that sounds something like this:

Clinician: Sit in a comfortable position... symmetrical and balanced... with your eyes open or closed... and just give yourself permission to listen... or not listen... to let your mind drift wherever it chooses to go.... If you notice what I'm saying, that's fine... and if you forget to listen, just let your mind wander and wonder about where it will take you.

While I guide you along... lulling you into a comfortable space... you may be curious... it's your job to notice what you notice... accept what you notice... and find your own way into the healing space.... Trust your own unconscious mind to seek and find information you already hold within.

What you find... that you already know... will guide you to rise up... stand tall... accept the change of perspective... and will help you to build new... healthy associations.

As you tune in with your attention inward... I will begin to count from one to ten.... As I count... notice whatever you notice.

[The formality of ceremoniously counting from one to ten delineates the trance induction within which I offered progressive relaxation using a Jacobson technique of tension and relaxation. After establishing a pattern of differentiating relaxation from tension, I then shifted to a remembrance of what tension and relaxation feel like.]

In your imagination... in your memory... but not in your body... feel your fists tighten... and then release.

[Again, and again emphasizing...]

You already know... you've already learned how... call upon that awareness held within your body... an awareness that is speaking in feelings... long forgotten... and now remembered.

[I also emphasize...]

Attend to your own breathing... noticing and appreciating how the body already knows how and when to take a deep breath... knows the refreshing feeling of oxygen circulating throughout the body and the sense of change that just a few deep breaths can bring. ... Yet, if you forget, your body remembers and establishes its own rhythm... a pattern that serves your needs... a rhythm that nourishes when needed and rests when needed. ... Appreciate that internal wisdom that you need not remember.

[As I use my words and voice to lull the patient into a receptive state, I immediately bring in deepening techniques to link the body to the experience.]

Right hand and left... left foot and right... knowing what is right from what needs left... leaving what needs left behind... that's right... a pitter patter of a pattern of familiar steps in learning to balance one step after another... one step at a time, deep into a state of comfort and relaxation, more comfortable each step of the way.

> *[The combination of permissive suggestion with confusing or ambiguous word use has a tendency to bring about a dissociative response which then facilitates greater suggestibility. Once the patient appears to be deeply relaxed, I then offer direct suggestions.]*

Find your own internal balance.

Listen to the messages within.

Respect the need to balance rest with the productivity of work.

Enjoy the feeling of a day of hard work.

Sensations felt within will express themselves in meaningful ways, giving you clarity on what needs to be attended to and what can be set aside.

You will find that each time you return to this space and place of healing, the pathway will become easier and the journey more healing.

You will soon remember that you had forgotten all about the discomfort that brought you here, and you will enjoy that future sense of peace in your present moment, a gift of time.

Upon re-arousal, if a patient has experienced an emotional release of tearfulness, I comment on this in a reassuring way. I only review the trance experience if the patient initiates discussion. I consistently ask patients if there is anything they wish to tell me at this time—but I discourage a long narrative over the trance experience. My sense is that conscious review can de-potentiate ongoing unconscious work. At the conclusion of a trance, I emphasize that the most important thing is for the patient to be completely awake to safely navigate their way home.

On subsequent visits, I invite patients to tell me whatever they wish about previous trance experiences. Once the patient has expressed what they choose to express about the trance, I shift to a cognitive discussion emphasizing responsibilities of eating well, establishing healthy sleep/rest patterns, maintaining reasonable activity level, and contributing in a positive way to society. I reinforce judicious use of pharmaceuticals and the responsibility to report accurately to members of the medical team.

Each follow-up visit I begin by inquiring whether there is anything they would like to say about the last hypnotic experience. Over the next few sessions with Joe I introduced guided imagery, which sets a stage for a multitude of indirect suggestions:

Walking through the woods... a rocky path with its ups and downs... the rough bark of older trees... trees that stand tall reaching for sunlight with branches connecting to those around... the rhythm of life in the community.

With Joe, as with other clients, I did not begin to shift responsibility to self-hypnosis until the fourth visit. My self-hypnosis teaching techniques include handouts and reviews of what to expect in self-hypnosis practice sessions. With Joe, he chose to have only five visits, which were widely spaced (several months apart). He reported satisfactory progress, and he kept the door open for returning for another "tune-up."

Although he expressed awareness for taking charge of his own self-hypnotic trance state, he preferred to "just let it happen." I would describe this case with Joe as an uncomplicated case with a motivated and receptive subject.

Working with him was especially rewarding in that I had repeated verbal follow up with him. The widely spaced visits allowed me to see that he had achieved what he had sought.

The complex case Erickson described, as well as the more limited case with Joe, both illustrate how hypnotic suggestion and trance experiences can qualitatively alter a patient's life. Erickson emphasized that hypnosis provides a plethora of tools to work with and that a flexible approach opens the door in an unlimited number of ways. He suggests that to best serve the patient, begin with an achievable goal so that the patient can enjoy a feeling of success.

Erickson urges us to,

> ...consider a total approach is possible. But more feasible is the utilization of hypnosis in relation first to minor aspects of the total pain complex and then to increasingly severe and distressing qualities. Thus, minor successes will lay a foundation for major successes in relation to the more distressing attributes of the neuro-psycho-physiological complex of pain and the understanding and cooperation of the patient for hypnotic intervention are more readily elicited. Additionally, any hypnotic alteration of any single interpretive quality of the pain sensation serves to effect an alteration of the total pain complex. (Rossi et al., 2014a, p. 97)

Our ongoing discoveries, including fearless self-reflection inclusive of successes, limitations, and unexpected outcomes, allow us to advance further, day-by-day and case-by-case. Working with a professional group, which includes open discussions about successes and provides ongoing learning opportunities, allows us to explore together further than we could advance individually. Erickson emphasized that there is no single right direction; it is a process of ongoing discovery.

> Hypnosis itself, what processes occur within the subject, in what manner the body alters its usual functioning, and out of what experiential learnings of the past the body so learned to function, all constitute a part of the exceedingly rich field for research in hypnosis. (Rossi et al., 2010b, p. 344)

The ways that health and symptoms express themselves in each individual is unique. It is incumbent upon the clinician to create an awareness, to listen attentively to what is expressed, and to encourage the patient to attend to signals that are being delivered. The internal attention and developing unconscious awareness of distinguishing what *is* significant from what *is not* significant leads to shifts of perception. The ongoing process of reflection, evaluation, exploration, and curiosity brings opportunities to enhance the healing process and to augment comfort. The exploration process itself can lead to a shift from suffering to comfort; a shift that can lead to enduring well-being.

References

Erickson-Klein, R. (1990). Pain control interventions of Milton H. Erickson. In J. Zeig & S. Gilligan, S. (Eds.), *Brief Therapy* (pp. 273-286). New York, NY: Brunner/Mazel.

Haley, J. (Ed.) (1985). *Conversations with Milton H. Erickson M.D. (Vol 1): Changing individuals.* New York, NY: Triangle Press.

Rossi, E., Erickson-Klein, R., & Rossi, K. (Eds). (2008a). *The collected works of Milton H. Erickson (Vol. 1): The nature of therapeutic hypnosis.* Phoenix, AZ: The Erickson Foundation Press.

Rossi, E., Erickson-Klein, R., & Rossi, K. (Eds). (2008b). *The collected works of Milton H. Erickson (Vol. 2): Basic hypnotic induction and suggestion.* Phoenix, AZ: The Erickson Foundation Press.

Rossi, E., Erickson-Klein, R., & Rossi, K. (Eds). (2008c). *The collected works of Milton H. Erickson (Vol. 3): Opening the mind: Innovative psychotherapy.* Phoenix, AZ: The Erickson Foundation Press.

Rossi, E., Erickson-Klein, R., & Rossi, K. (Eds). (2008d). *The collected works of Milton H. Erickson (Vol. 4): Advanced approaches to therapeutic hypnosis.* Phoenix, AZ: The Erickson Foundation Press.

Rossi, E., Erickson-Klein, R., & Rossi, K. (Eds). (2009). *The collected works of Milton H. Erickson (Vol. 9): The February man.* Phoenix, AZ: The Erickson Foundation Press.

Rossi, E., Erickson-Klein, R., & Rossi, K. (Eds). (2010a). *The collected works of Milton H. Erickson (Vol. 5): Classic hypnotic phenomena, Part 1: Psychodynamics.* Phoenix, AZ: The Erickson Foundation Press.

Rossi, E., Erickson-Klein, R., & Rossi, K. (Eds). (2010b). *The collected works of Milton H. Erickson (Vol. 6): Classic hypnotic phenomena, Part 2: Memory and hallucination.* Phoenix, AZ: The Erickson Foundation Press.

Rossi, E., Erickson-Klein, R., & Rossi, K. (Eds). (2010c). *The collected works of Milton H. Erickson (Vol. 7): Mind-body healing and rehabilitation.* Phoenix, AZ: The Erickson Foundation Press.

Rossi, E., Erickson-Klein, R., & Rossi, K. (Eds). (2010d). *The collected works of Milton H. Erickson (Vol. 8): General and historical surveys of hypnosis.* Phoenix, AZ: The Erickson Foundation Press.

Rossi, E., Erickson-Klein, R., & Rossi, K. (Eds). (2010e). *The collected works of Milton H. Erickson (Vol. 10): Hypnotic realities.* Phoenix, AZ: The Erickson Foundation Press.

Rossi, E., Erickson-Klein, R., & Rossi, K. (Eds). (2014a). *The collected works of Milton H. Erickson (Vol. 11): Hypnotherapy: An exploratory casebook.* Phoenix, AZ: The Erickson Foundation Press.

Rossi, E., Erickson-Klein, R., & Rossi, K. (Eds). (2014b). *The collected works of Milton H. Erickson (Vol. 12): Experiencing hypnosis: Therapeutic approaches to altered states.* Phoenix, AZ: The Erickson Foundation Press.

Rossi, E., Erickson-Klein, R., & Rossi, K. (Eds). (2014c). *The collected works of Milton H. Erickson (Vol. 13): Healing in hypnosis: Seminars, workshops and lectures, Part 1.* Phoenix, AZ: The Erickson Foundation Press.

Rossi, E., Erickson-Klein, R., & Rossi, K. (Eds). (2014d). *The collected works of Milton H. Erickson (Vol. 14): Life reframing in hypnosis: Seminars, workshops and lectures, Part 2.* Phoenix, AZ: The Erickson Foundation Press.

Rossi, E., Erickson-Klein, R., & Rossi, K. (Eds). (2015a). *The collected works of Milton H. Erickson (Vol. 15): Mind-body communication in hypnosis: Seminars, workshops and lectures, Part 3.* Phoenix, AZ: The Erickson Foundation Press.

Rossi, E., Erickson-Klein, R., & Rossi, K. (Eds). (2015b). *The collected works of Milton H. Erickson (Vol. 16): Creative choice in hypnosis: Seminars, workshops and lectures, Part 4.* Phoenix, AZ: The Erickson Foundation Press.

Short, D. (Ed.). (2017). *Principles and core competencies of Ericksonian therapy.* Unpublished manuscript. Available at: http://iamdrshort.com/PDF/Papers/Core%20Competencies%20Manual.pdf

CHAPTER 11

Hypnosis in Multidisciplinary Chronic Pain Treatment

Miyuki Mizutani

Miyuki Mizutani is a clinical psychologist working in the Multidisciplinary Pain Center at Aichi Medical University in Aichi, Japan, since its establishment in 2007. She has been dedicated to exploring the use of hypnosis for patients with refractory chronic pain since she interviewed 12 patients with complex regional pain syndrome (CRPS) type I at the Department of Anesthesiology at Nagoya University in Aichi, Japan, over 19 years ago. She learned that refractory pain is maintained by a vicious cycle of biological, psychological, and social factors, which cannot be adequately treated using interventions that target only one of these components; some truly refractory pain problems require an intervention that will stop the core of the vicious cycle—the pain itself. Since she started clinical research on the use of hypnosis for refractory chronic pain, she has learned to be sensitive to the importance of using a certain approach in hypnotic treatment, and she identified some key principles of hypnotic analgesia that underlie tailored hypnosis for individual practice. She hopes that sharing her clinical experiences—both successful and unsuccessful—will provide a basis for better practice and scientific research on hypnosis for chronic pain. She is currently a visiting scholar at Aichi Medical University and serves on the Council of the Japanese Society of Clinical Hypnosis.

* * *

The complexity of chronic pain as a target of treatment was first recognized by John J. Bonica (Liebeskind et al., 1994). At that time, it was known that a purely biomedical approach to treatment was not effective for the patients who were developing chronic pain. However, there was not yet research literature about the diagnosis or management of chronic pain (Liebeskind et al., 1994). Treatments that might be used instead of the (ineffective) biomedical approaches were not available at the time.

To address the need for a treatment approach that would reflect the complexity of chronic pain, Dr. Bonica invented the concept of multidisciplinary pain treatment and established the first multidisciplinary pain center (MPC) in 1978 (Liebeskind et al., 1994; Loeser, 2017; Zimmermann, 2005). In this MPC, psychological treatments, from what was at the time mainstream psychotherapy, were introduced as a key treatment component. These treatments included behavioral methods to modify pain-related behaviors, as well as cognitive behavioral therapy (CBT) to modify responses to pain by changing the patients' appraisals and response options through self-instruction (Morley & Williams, 2015).

CBT is now established as an effective psychological treatment for chronic pain. It is widely utilized by physicians, nurses, and physiotherapists as well as by psychologists to help patients to better cope with and manage pain. In our MPC, which includes medication management, nerve blocks, exercise therapy, and CBT, approximately 60% of patients report substantial improvements in pain at three months after the first visit; about 35% report no change, and about 5% report that their pain is worse.

Only a small subset of the most refractory patients (about 5% during the first year of our MPC) were initially referred by the attending doctors to a clinical psychologist for individual psychotherapy. At that time, these patients reported a statistically significant but perhaps clinically limited reduction in pain from 7.9 (on a 0-10 scale, with 0 = "No pain" and 10 = "Worst pain imaginable") when biomedical treatment started, to 6.8 at the time they were referred for psychotherapy. Thus, I thought hypnosis might serve these patients' needs, given that hypnosis had been shown to be a safe and practical method for pain treatment before modern medicine (Gauld, 1995). However, there were (and still are) few reports of hypnosis targeting pain itself in the context of multidisciplinary pain treatment.

In my hypnotic work with patients who have refractory pain, I consider and address more than just pain; I am also concerned with the patient's daily life, because a healthy lifestyle, including adequate exercise, helps prevent the recurrence and exacerbation of chronic pain.

A Hypnotic Strategy for
Refractory Chronic Pain Management

The strategy for "hypnotic analgesia" is to help the patients to create non-pain experiences in a way that is least demanding to the patient. Patients with refractory chronic pain often have difficulty responding to hypnotic suggestions that directly influence pain (i.e., to decrease pain intensity or to change the location or quality of the pain) or that shift attention from pain. In addition, creating or nurturing comfortable imagery that helps the patient feel distant from his or her present (pain) state can also be challenging, at least in the beginning of treatment. These patients often feel too helpless and too confused to accept hypnosis and to focus their attention effectively for the alleviation of pain.

Thus, non-pain experiences need to be created by somatic suggestions which utilize breathing, ideomotor responses, or proprioception, given that our "pain experience" is neither a nociception itself nor a mere sensation. Rather, pain involves spinal reflexes (Kumazawa, 1991), autonomic responses (Bantel & Trapp, 2011), and emotional meaning (and thoughts) related to survival, defense, and social isolation—the whole of which is generally experienced as pain. Therefore, the ongoing process to create non-pain experiences during the session needs to involve the links with each patient's own pain experience. In my experience, the non-pain experience is analgesic only when the patient's pain experience has been vividly shared between the patient and the clinician, and its negative meaning is somewhat altered prior to the induction.

I think it is particularly important to be aware of the patient's experiences with respect to the medical setting. By definition, these patients have failed to respond to medical treatments and many have not responded successfully to training in adaptive coping skills such as walking, exercise programs, or positive self-statements. They often believe that their pain is a (permanent) substantial entity embedded in themselves and as a result they feel truly *helpless*.

In addition, in the medical setting chronic pain is often viewed as an incurable condition which needs to be managed. Thus, patients might have been told they need to—or they may have tried themselves to—cope more effectively with their pain or to distract their attention from pain. Such a situation represents an ongoing suggestion for the patient to have chronic and unchangeable pain. The development of refractory chronic pain is also intrinsically threatening and stigmatic, and patient's experiences with chronic pain can be chaotic and can make them feel hopeless.

Over the years, I have learned to address chronic refractory pain by thinking in terms of two *processes* in each session: (1) an introduction process and (2) an induction process. I have also learned that successful changes in chronic refractory pain proceed as follows: (1) an initial phase that lasts until a decrease in pain is experienced for the first time, usually within a treatment session, and (2) a second phase that lasts until the patient experiences a decrease in daily chronic pain for the first time.

Two Processes in a Treatment Session

The Introduction Process

The goals for the introduction process are to alleviate helplessness, confusion, and chaos in the patient's own pain experience and consequently to link it with the ongoing process *therapeutically*. The principle procedure begins during the initial patient interview, when I seek to understand in-depth the patient's present pain state and pain history; how the pain started and developed and how the patient has been living with the pain.

The patient needs to be listened to carefully, personally, and acceptingly; to feel free to talk about their pain experiences, including past and present treatments. When the patient gets absorbed in talking and recalling, the clinician can learn about the core issues related to their suffering and the personal meaning of the pain from the patient's perspective.

The initial onset episode of pain and the treatment history reveal important characteristics of the pain such as: (1)

fluctuation in intensity, (2) responsiveness to medications (such as nonsteroidal anti-inflammatory drugs and opioids) and other pain treatments, (3) disparities between subjective severity and medical evaluations, (4) pain coping, (5) misconceptions about pain, and (6) the level of compliance with treatment recommendations.

The onset episode and the following events are often associated with traumatic events, important life events, or core lifelong struggles. Information about these issues often reveals a certain extremeness or extraordinary efforts in the patient's way of thinking or living, the patient's relationships with others, and the relation of these to the pain problem. The information obtained here is useful for understanding the patient and his or her sensory experience, as well as the development of chronic pain.

The clinician first helps the patient discriminate the present from the past regarding the onset of pain by careful use of the past and present tense. The clinician invites the patient to appreciate his or her own efforts and values, which may have gone unnoticed by the patient over the course of time. Here, as always, the clinician avoids a judgmental stance and seeks to affirm the patient just as he or she is.

A second goal of the introduction process is to help the patient to understand the contribution of psychosomatic tension (and pain memory) to pain, as well as the contribution of inappropriate coping behaviors, such as avoidance or hyperactivity, to deconditioning and to the overall experience of pain and to suffering. Patients with refractory chronic pain often believe that they have some (as yet) undetected or undiagnosed biomedical (and ultimately curable) cause of the pain, despite the fact that they are often told by their health care providers that this is not the case. Alternatively, they may have been told that they have incurable causes of their pain. For these reasons, a subset of patients *do* accept hypnosis as a viable treatment, while another subset of patients have difficulty in accepting hypnosis, assuming hypnosis is useless for their "real" pain or fearing that their pain might be considered as fake if they respond to hypnotic suggestion.

On the other hand, and for some patients, the idea that muscle tension is contributing to their pain may be more acceptable than the idea that pain is ultimately constructed in the brain. (Actually, both are biologically correct.) If they accept one or both of these ideas, this can function as rationale for possible change in the present pain and for learning new skills that will ultimately result in a change in their pain, which they view as a part of themselves.

Throughout treatment, negative ideas and suggestions are deliberately avoided, and pain is referred to as something which can change (i.e., it is *not* chronic) and which is not a substantial entity (i.e., it is not another word for nociception), with due consideration given to the patient's doubts or hesitation. Even if or when a patient makes a statement that is incorrect or unhelpful, rather than confronting the patient, the clinician can say something along the lines of, "At present, it is natural that you would think so." Even if the patient is not yet ready to accept the idea of hypnotic analgesia consciously, he or she is likely ready to participate in a hypnotic induction process, having been absorbed in talking and sharing his or her experience during the introduction process.

The Induction Process

The end goal of the session is to create a non-pain experience which leads to analgesia automatically. A key strategy is to facilitate self-efficacy and the awareness of body sensations and physical comfort. At this stage, the patient may still be vulnerable to feelings of disappointment with treatment, although ideally some degree of helplessness will have been alleviated during the introduction process. Importantly, any non-pain experience should be experienced as "automatic" rather than "with effort."

The suggestion to "relax yourself" is often not enough, because many patients with refractory chronic pain have forgotten how to relax themselves. They tend to be unaware of their own body sensations and may not notice tight muscles or uncomfortable body postures. They also sometimes have an impaired ability to experience the sensations of warmth or touch. Patients with such conditions often have a history of "extreme situations" or "extraordinary efforts" in daily life or in relationships with others, or they may have a history of a severely painful injury or disease.

Hypnotic suggestions should take into account the patient's current experiences and emotional states and from there proceed to become either neutral or positive. In cases where the patient begins the session in a negative state, his or her hypnotic experience may also be negative (and therefore not analgesic). When I first began using hypnosis with individuals with chronic pain, some patients felt worse following the induction (for example, feeling like they were falling down or twisted around); responses which were related to the emotion that the patient had during the introduction process.

Thus, it is important that during the introduction process, the patient is encouraged to focus on talking and is gently encouraged to shift from a negative mood to a neutral or positive mood. Then, as the patient begins to show signs of or interest in trance (e.g., a decrease in spontaneous movements, or by asking what hypnosis is like) it is time to start the induction.

The first suggestion of the induction should be related to what is actually happening with the patient at the moment the suggestion is made. The suggestions may help the patient to assume a comfortable position or to breathe at a rate that is comfortable. Breathing can be suggested to be both volitional (at first) and automatic (as the induction progresses), although of course it is an autonomic process (i.e., it is controlled not only by metabolic demands but also constantly responds to changes in emotion). The clinician can encourage the patient to focus inward and then to shift from a volitional to an involuntary state, towards parasympathetic (i.e., relaxed) responding.

As the inward focus narrows and deepens, the suggestions can increasingly have a personal meaning for each patient. For example, a patient who is lost in rumination may have suppressed breathing. A patient who had a cruel mother may have lost the ability to experience the proprioceptive sensation of warmth. Suggestions are given for such bodily reactions and sensations (e. g., direct approaches such as "breathing *deeply*..." or "feeling the *warm* sensations...," utilization of spontaneous cataleptic responses, or the suggestion to "feel the warmth of my [i.e., the clinician's] hand..."). Such suggestions, during the induction, can both affirm and ameliorate the patient's extreme responses and suffering, or they can symbolically reaffirm a core patient value. This begins the process of creating a non-pain experience, which is closely related to, but is not the same as, the present pain experience.

The patient's own ability to create a non-pain experience incompatible with the chronic pain experience then results in a distinct analgesic experience, which I call in-session analgesia (ISA). It requires that the analgesic non-pain experience be maintained for more than 15 minutes in order to be established as a sustainable experience that lasts beyond the hypnotic session. At this stage, some patients describe spontaneous imagery.

In order to maintain this non-pain state for as long as possible, the clinician can provide affirmative suggestions. The clinician might, for example, suggest imagery or experiences that would be symbolic and therapeutic for the patient, such as comfortable mountain walking, observing a steadily growing tree, or awareness of the peaceful cycles in nature. Importantly, every so often any successful responses are attributed to the patient's inner potential and skills, both as a suggestion and as a fact.

The Two Phases of Change:
In-Session Analgesia and Out-of-Session Analgesia

As a result of a successful introduction process and induction process during the treatment session, a decrease in pain is experienced during the session (in-session analgesia, or ISA). The number of sessions necessary for the first ISA to occur depends on the patient's readiness to achieve the goals of the introduction and induction processes. The hesitancy about the use of hypnosis or the suppressed state of body sensations as the basis of response to suggestions here might block ISA. I have observed that the mean number of sessions necessary for ISA has been about four (with a very large variability from patient to patient). My goal is to achieve ISA by at least the tenth session in order to maintain the patient's motivation to continue with treatment.

Statements regarding the degree of analgesia differ markedly among patients, including: "I felt nothing and thought nothing," "My pain has gone," "I felt the stabbing pain disappear," and "It is a little bit better."

The first ISA may maintain for just a few minutes or as long as a month. However, *the patient who can experience ISA can also learn self-hypnosis and can ultimately experience out-of-session analgesia (OSA)*. The repeated experiences of analgesia, whether by self-hypnosis or during sessions, result in the decreased baseline level of pain (i.e., OSA). In fact, the decrease by even two points on the 0-10 Numerical Rating Scale in ISA is clinically meaningful for developing OSA. I have found that the mean number of sessions necessary for OSA following the first ISA is also four. Even after the first OSA is attained, pain might recur under the influence of triggering biopsychosocial factors or events, which cannot always be totally eliminated in one session. Therefore, each session should include an introduction process to help guide the suggestions that will be offered following the induction process. ISA is created for the present pain. OSA is attained for the chronic condition.

For example, the involvement of the autonomic nervous system and muscle tension is more or less conditioned in the patient and may require time to be attenuated. In these cases, the improvement of mood might precede the first ISA. Another patient might not be able to notice the influence of stressful events or emotions on pain. Therefore, the clinician needs to be aware of the time course of any changes in pain, taking into account the type of pain and coexisting biopsychosocial factors. It is also important to be encouraging of patients whose first ISA is delayed, as well as of those patients who have a recurrence and exacerbation of pain after the first OSA.

So, the clinician might explain the time course of changes in pain, or say to the patient whose OSA is delayed, "When you are driving a car at 100km/hour, you might not notice at first when the speed begins to decrease, even if the speed had gone down to 95 or 90km/hour. But you might notice when it is 70, or 80km/hour? You would surely notice if it drops to 60km/hour." Or, to the patient whose pain got worse after the first OSA, "Once a person experiences improvements, he or she might notice a small recurrence, and at first view it as a very bad exacerbation. And can you identify some stressful events or ideas which have influenced your pain this time?"

In our pain center, about 70% of the patients who proceed to the induction process experience ISA. OSA is then experienced by approximately 65% of these patients. In short, I have found hypnosis to be an effective treatment for the majority of patients with refractory chronic pain, when they accept hypnosis.

For the patients with refractory chronic pain, hypnotic analgesia is not only a coping skill. Analgesic experiences during the sessions and with self-hypnosis help patients recover their psychophysiological abilities, such as the relaxation response, and to recover normal sensations. It takes some time (and practice) for patients to begin to experience pain as controllable, and for them to be able to use self-hypnosis as a psychophysiological coping skill. During this process, they experience an increase in self-efficacy for pain control; they are also likely to reduce their catastrophic thinking about pain.

So, when a patient says to the clinician following hypnosis treatment, "I do not worry about pain these days," the clinician can say, "Yes, your pain problem has changed—it has improved because of your brain's potential. And this ability is a part of your inborn nature."

In the remainder of this chapter, I present some examples of transcripts. The first is a typical session with a patient who has difficulty in sitting due to her pain. The second transcript presents a variety of ideas that do not necessarily need to be offered to the same patient, but it includes examples of a variety of suggestions which can be dropped or rearranged, depending on the needs of the patient. For example, the breathing component is useful for many patients and it can even be enough by itself for some. On the other hand, if the patient finds this component difficult, it can be reduced or eliminated and replaced with the other components, perhaps used again at a subsequent session if indicated.

Transcript One:
Dialogue with your Body—Eliciting and Accepting

Clinician: Would you tell me how it started?

[Eliciting the narrative about the onset of pain.]

Patient: It was an accident in my workplace. ... A long tray hit me in the right arm and I twisted my torso. I don't know how it happened. It was so painful that I wanted to call an ambulance, but it was also such a busy time...

Clinician: Even when it hurt so much, you considered your colleagues and did not want to inconvenience them.

Patient: It has always been difficult for me to say, "It hurts," ever since my childhood.

Clinician: Can you say, "It hurts," these days?

Patient: No.

Clinician: It's sad. ... Has your pain gotten any better since the initial onset?

[Discriminating between the past and present as a frame of change and specifying the direction of change.]

Patient: I think the initial pain has decreased a little, but it still lingers, even now, four years after the injury. And the medications are no longer effective.

Clinician: That means the pain medications had worked well at first, and the tissues that had been injured, which were the cause of acute pain, are now healed. Now, here you are, and you continue to experience pain, which is not uncommon after an injury

[Dispelling misconceptions and providing therapeutic order to the patient's chaotic understanding of pain and treatment.]

Patient: Do you think my pain will get better?

Clinician: Yes. It is my role here to help you do that. How are you getting by these days?

Patient: I work part-time and I accompany my mother to the hospital. I do not have much to do these days, compared to when my children were in primary school.

Clinician: So, you are clearly doing a good "job." And, you have always been doing a good "job."

Patient: Well, maybe so; but also maybe not.

Clinician: But the "job" must have been very hard.

[Eliciting narrative and inviting the patient to appreciate his or her own efforts. The "job" is not merely work at one's place of employment or performance at school but anything

the patient has been engaged in. The clinician seeks to affirm and not to judge the patient.]

Clinician: What is your daily life like with the pain? Do you wake up from sleep in pain? Does it sometimes happen that you notice that the pain isn't there? Does it hurt when you move?

[Eliciting information and listening carefully, in order to get a sense of the patient's pain. Taking enough time to ensure that the patient feels that his or her pain is understood by the therapist.]

Patient: I awake from sleep with a sharp pain in the right side of my body, several times a night, almost every night. Certainly, I do my job, working on light duty in the workplace. I take my dog for a walk or take my mother to the hospital. But I always have pain in the right side of my body from my head to my leg.

Clinician: You have this pain, and you also know how to cope with the pain. Generally, it's good for you to walk, when you feel you can. Appropriate walking or exercise improves blood flow, muscle flexibility, and overall health. And you will be aware in due time that improvements in your health and comfort are coming. Or your body tension might interfere with such benefits.

[Inserting provocative and helpful suggestions and pain education during history taking. It is important to notice how the patient responds to the information and suggestions provided. If they are nodding and agreeing, then the information and suggestions can continue to be useful. When or if the patient appears to or starts to disagree, then the clinician should "tone down" the provision of information and suggestions at this stage.]

Clinician: Do you feel comfort when you soak in a nice, hot bath?

Patient: Not at all. The steam chokes me. I can't relax myself. I can't take a deep breath. Even sitting on a chair is painful.

Clinician: Let's start. Here is a bed. You can use it if you would like.

[The clinician is helping the patient with therapeutic positioning.]

Patient: No. lying down is even more painful for me.
Clinician: Would you stand up? Let me see... or would you sit down? ... OK... Now... how about this height?

[Note: The clinician adjusts the height of the chair and offers it to the patient.]

Does that feel better?

[The clinician assesses the patient's response to the different height of chair.]

Patient: No. My right leg hurts even more. When I am sitting, I can't put weight on my left foot. So, I can't ease my right leg.

[The pain in the right leg seems difficult to explain mechanically and might be related to a psychophysiological or "psychomechanical" imbalance.]

Clinician: Then, shall we stand instead? ... That's fine. ... May I touch your back, very lightly? ... Do you feel that? ... Do you feel its warmth?

[Here the clinician shows caring and sincere interest about the patient's pain experience and facilitates participation and inward focus. The clinician also assesses the patient's sensory

*awareness and facilitates a focus on sensory experience, as
well as on the distinction between the right and left.]*

**Patient: I feel warmth in the left side but it feels
uncomfortable. The right side is painful.**

[Allodynia or hyperalgesia on the affected side.]

**Clinician: Just focus on standing... as easy as possible... for
yourself. ... My hands are not touching your back... and
whenever necessary, my hands are there, ready to support
you. ... That's right... standing with your feet apart at a
distance that is best for you... and as you feel it... you can
focus more easily in this way... just for yourself... you are
standing... a little bit differently from usual... and you are
noticing... your body is beginning to sway.... That's fine....
You can allow it to sway.... And you are noticing... it is
natural... as you sway... you notice... you can let it go... for
yourself... a little bit relaxed... and you also can sit down...
whenever you would like to...**

*[The patient has entered trance. The clinician is describing
what is going on and solacing the patient's endurance,
simultaneously. The patient's body begins "postural sway"
back and forth. And based on the clinician's observations,
suggestions are given to help the patient focus on and
experience more sensory experiences. Care is taken lest the
patient make excessive effort.]*

Patient: Yes, I am feeling a little bit better.

**Clinician: Okay. ... Let's sit down... and you feel better
now.**

**Patient: Yes, the left leg is now lighter, but the right side is
still heavy...**

[The clinician notices that the left shoulder is kept higher than the right shoulder. The patient's hands appear to be cataleptic, with the left hand softly enclosing the right hand, on her lap.]

Clinician: Do you notice... how the right hand is touched... and enfolded by the left hand... so softly... delicately... and really gently? ... Are you noticing the gentleness and warmth... where the hands are touching one another? ... And the hands are getting a little bit warmer... and warmer a little bit... and the left shoulder is getting loose... it is starting to become lower... and you are feeling relaxed...

[Narrowing the patient's focus. Facilitating the sensory experience of warmth, which she needs.]

Patient: Oh, yes. I can breathe deeply... I can take deep breaths...

[The patient has become aware of a non-pain body sensation that she has created.]

Clinician: That's fine. You are fine... you are doing really well...

Transcript Two:
Dialogue with your Body—Observing and Orienting

Clinician: It is not necessary to believe at this moment that... as you enter hypnosis... and experience analgesia in hypnosis... as soon as you enter... it is absolutely desirable to proceed at your own pace and in your own way... by your own choice, listening to my voice...

[Therapeutic bind.]

Once it happens, subtly or obviously, your body remembers the experience.

[The body's role is emphasized and the patient's responsibility is mitigated.]

Patient: What is hypnosis like?

Clinician: Hypnosis is a natural experience... actually it is a natural ability of human brain. What happens if you find a lemon on the table in front of you... you imagine and see a lemon on the table... you pick it up and... cutting with a knife... and just biting with your teeth? ... Perhaps you cannot stop salivating even if you would try to stop salivating... once you see a fresh yellow lemon...

[When the clinician notices the patient is increasingly focused on talking, often with nodding, and his or her negative mood has been ameliorated, it is time to start the induction.]

Whatever you experience is a result of your brain's ability... when it happens, you cannot stop it. ... So, let it go as it happens. The only thing you have to do is to... listen to my voice and... feel your body feel... what I say.

[Automaticity is emphasized.]

As you sit on the chair like this, allow yourself to get into a comfortable position.

That's fine... and go ahead... and let go of your shoulder.... You are noticing now. ... Your shoulder was tight. ... Now, breathing is a little bit easier. ... You inhale through the nose... and exhale through the mouth.

[The patient's focus has turned inward, and he or she is now aware of bodily sensations.]

A little bit of dry, fresh air... is coming in through your nose... and a little bit of warm, moist air... is going out through your mouth. ... The air coming in is slightly dry and cool... the air going out is slightly warm. ... The mouth is open slightly... and the air is going out... running between the upper teeth... and the lower teeth.

[Adjusting the timing of suggestions with the patient's breathing.]

As you breathe out... you feel muscles loosen... from the neck through the shoulder... to the arms and to the fingertips. ... As the breath goes out... you feel any tightness is melting away... from the neck to the back...

[The focus of awareness is gradually widened from around the mouth to the torso.]

As the breath goes out... you feel the body relax. ... As the breath comes in... you feel the body fill up... (as you exhale) relaxing... (and as you inhale) filling with fresh air... a ball of breath... (as you exhale), like a ball in slow motion... going down, reaching the floor... staying for a moment... and... naturally bouncing up... touching your palm... and then pushing down again... and bouncing up, naturally...

It falls down... and bounces up... between the floor and your palm...

[The breath as "an object" shifts to "an internal experience" involving the patient's body movement and unified with the breathing; inducing the patient to breathe gradually deeper. Alternating voluntary movements and involuntary automatic movements establishes therapeutic automaticity. The trance is deepened naturally, without special effort.]

The ball falls down... to the most comfortable point... stays there for a moment... and bounces up... fitting into your palm... at the most comfortable point...

[If the patient's breathing is observed to be irregular, the clinician can add,]

And you might wonder... where the most comfortable point is...

[If the patient's breathing appears a little bit awkward, or a little too shallow or too deep, the clinician can add,]

so you breathe to the point just before it is too much, or to the point just after it is not quite enough... and at your own pace.

[If the patient makes movements suggesting discomfort or ambivalence about the experience, the clinician can add suggestions for reassuring the patient, such as,]

So, you might wonder where the most comfortable point is... and it's all right. You have all the time you need... just continue this breathing... wondering, where is the most comfortable point? ... That's fine... and you are doing very well...

[The extremes are being reconciled. The patient is in control and also lets go of control. He or she is learning bodily that he or she does not need to make an effort to "cope"—it happens automatically.]

The fresh air is coming in, and warm air is going out, as you are aware of the warmth of the breath... you feel the warmth of yourself... there's a core of your energy... around the back of your stomach... it is a fountain of energy... always available... it will never dry up, no matter how much it is used... the warm energy flow goes around... around your body... throughout your body... to your fingertips... to your toes... so you might have felt... or you might feel... your fingertips are thicker... or your toes are tingling a little bit...

[Self-efficacy is bodily experienced. The chaos is over.]

As you become more aware of yourself, any tension... is melting away... warmly... and lightly... more and more. ... Any tension is melting away... all down the back... from your neck... to the bottom. ... And from your neck through your shoulders... and from your arms... through your fingers... relaxed... and the body is so relaxed... you feel yourself.

[As the patient responds to the suggestions, he or she learns how his or her body is his or her own and how it is comfortable. Any tension has already decreased; therefore, the patient can safely accept the effects of hypnosis as his or her own ability.]

You are sitting on the chair... you can feel your body resting on the seat... and as you feel... you can trust it to the chair... the body settles down... reassuringly. You feel the soles of the feet... the bottom of the shoes and the floor. As you feel this... you can leave the feet on the floor... solid on the ground... relaxed... very relaxed.

[Taking enough time to move focus to a body part which is far from the brain.]

Are you noticing your body is tilting to the left? ... If it's uncomfortable, you can move it... yes, like that... you just move, automatically, in order to feel the balance... and... the comfort... and you feel everything. You are doing very well... you and your body are learning to be aware... of the tension... to instantly move to the comfort... naturally... truly naturally, and instantly the tension melts away... as soon as you notice.

[The therapist is observing and encouraging the patient's safety, comfort, and increasing self-efficacy.]

Are you noticing your hands are getting warm?

[Usually, a relaxation response has been attained and the patient nods. However, occasionally the patient does not nod.]

Or, the surface is cool. ... The warmth may be deep inside... waiting and preparing, or getting ready to be warm.

The hands have the reins... the reins are in your hands... the reins of your body... you take the reins... softly... and feel that sensation... and you can use the reins whenever it's necessary to help guide the direction you take... the hands are warm... or a little bit warm at this moment... it's because your autonomic nervous system is working... to dilate the blood vessels... fresh warm blood is now reaching the tips of your fingers and... your toes... and moving throughout your body... whether you notice or not.

[Giving the patient choice is important. Creating a little tension and then releasing it very "softly." The balance of control and trust in automaticity is important.]

You can keep going... you are doing very well. You do not need to do anything special... because everything you do is special... as your body knows... and it keeps going.... Your body is always working... as you chose what you want. You feel this moment... as you feel your body feel... the experience remains in your body... your body remembers.

[Enhancing trust in the body.]

Your body remembers all the things that are necessary... whenever they are necessary... it allows you to breathe...

refreshing deep breaths... and as you do it... instantly, your body does... all the things necessary for you... your body does all that is necessary.

And you can have this experience whenever you need, even when any pain becomes worse temporarily. So, taking a deep breath whenever you need, this experience (of comfort... and control)... instantly comes back. Even if you are not consciously aware of it, the memory of the experience is deep in your body. This experience is now a part of you, whether you are conscious or unconscious of it.

> [Emphasizing the flexibility, automaticity, and trust in the body, as well as the patient's choice. The progression is suggested as a simple fact, and an explanation is added as a posthypnotic suggestion, to prevent nullification of analgesic suggestion following the common occurrence of (temporary) relapse.]

And now I am going to count to five from one. And you are going to come back, truly refreshed.

One. You hear the sounds around you.

Two. Your strength comes back to your hands and feet.

Three. Your strength comes back to your whole body.

Four. You take a deep breath... and exhale strongly.

Five. You take another deep breath... and exhale strongly. Stretching yourself, comfortably, and when your hands come back to your lap, you can open your eyes.

References

Bantel, C., & Trapp, S. (2011). The role of the autonomic nervous system in acute surgical pain processing: What do we know? *Anaesthesia, 66,* 541–544.

Gauld, A. (1995). *A history of hypnotism*. Cambridge, United Kingdom: Cambridge University Press.

Kumazawa, T. (1991). Biosensing mechanisms for noxious environments. *Environmental Medicine, 35*, 1–16.

Liebeskind, J. C., Merskey, H., Molina, F. J., Procacci, P., Short, C. E., & Swerdlow, M. (1994). In remembrance of John and Emma Bonica. *Pain, 59*, 425–427.

Loeser, J. D. (2017). John J. Bonica: Born 100 years ago. *Pain, 158*, 1845–1846.

Morley, S., & Williams, A. (2015). New Developments in the psychological management of chronic pain. *Canadian Journal of Psychiatry/Revue Canadienne de Psychiatrie, 60*, 168–175.

Zimmermann, M. (2005). History of pain concepts and treatment. In M. Harold, L. J. D, & D. Ronald (Eds.), *The paths of pain* (pp. 1–21). Seattle, WA: IASP Press.

For Further Reading

Mizutani, M. (2006). Hypnotically structured autogenic training applied to CRPS type I patients. *Japanese Journal of Hypnosis, 49*, 7–19.

Mizutani, M. (2012). Pain control by hypnosis: Empirical examination. *Japanese Journal of Hypnosis, 54*, 32–56.

Mizutani, M. (2014). Hypnosis for phantom limb pain after a root avulsion injury of brachial plexus. *Japanese Journal of Clinical Hypnosis, 15*, 6–17.

Mizutani, M. (2015). A need of a common set of descriptors for hypnosis in the treatment of pain. *Japanese Journal of Hypnosis, 55*, 1–9.

Mizutani, M. (2015). Hypnotic self-control of chronic pain: An attempt to describe low back pain in a young man. *Japanese Journal of Hypnosis, 55*, 10–22.

Mizutani, M., Suzuki, C., Omichi, Y., Sakurai, H., Morimoto, A., Nishihara, M., ... Sato, J. (2012). Psychotherapy for chronic pain in multidisciplinary pain center: Its indication and its effect. *Pain Research, 27*, 175–188.

Mizutani, M., Ushida, T., & Nishihara, M. (2017). Hypnotic approach for chronic pain patients in a multidisciplinary pain center. *Pain Research, 32*, 191–202.

CHAPTER 12

Resonance Based Medicine: A Systems Perspective for Managing Chronic Pain

Hansjörg Ebell

Hansjörg Ebell considers the implementation of hypnosis and self-hypnosis to be both fitting and invaluable when dealing with chronic illness (especially chronic pain and cancer) in the context of medical care. This conviction evolved pragmatically over years through his studied application of hypnotic phenomena in anesthesiology (1976-80), intensive care medicine (1980-83), interdisciplinary pain therapy at Munich University Clinic (1983-92), and, since 1992, in his psychotherapeutic practice. Dr. Ebell's publications on clinical issues regarding pain therapy and psycho-oncology include a controlled clinical study: Self-hypnosis as adjunct to pain therapy according to WHO guidelines with cancer patients, 1988-91. Further papers on psychotherapeutic support of chronically ill patients, most of them written in German, can be found on his website (www.doktorebell.de).

* * *

Chronic Pain and Medical Practice

Acute pain can be resolved when the cause has been treated sufficiently and/or its inherent homeostatic regulation has been addressed. However, what can be done when pain and disability persist, either with or without knowledge of the underlying cause? What if medical interventions prove themselves unable to cure, promote healing, or alleviate pain? What if therapeutic interventions themselves, i.e., treatments that are meant to help, make the condition worse? In recent decades, the suffering associated with chronic pain has been presented more and more as a "symptom," to be acknowledged and treated in the medical system as a discrete "disease." The predominant biomedical approach of "find it and fix it" needs to undertake a shift towards a more complex bio-psycho-social model in order to effectively support adaptive coping and self-management.

Adequate treatment of chronic pain requires a high degree of diagnostic and therapeutic competency to be able to identify the underlying pathophysiological factors and psycho-social issues. Clinicians must be able to both identify treatments that facilitate pain relief and to determine how to empower patients to learn to independently manage their pain more effectively. At the same time, clinicians need to be aware of the danger of promoting a patient's helplessness and dependence. This can be prevented through recognition of the simple fact that the patient's subjective experience of *"being ill"* (German: Krank*sein*) is of no less importance than the therapist's objective classification of *"illness"* (German: Krank*heit*; see Sauerbruch & Wenke, 1936, p. 76).

Both perspectives refer to the same condition. They are comparable to the perspective on a landscape in and of itself, and to the perspective of a map that illustrates certain aspects of the landscape, such as roads, population, and/or vegetation. If clinicians and patients work together in a *therapeutic alliance in resonance,* each with the expertise that stems from their specific point of view, they can collaboratively develop the most effective treatment plan. Putting this interventional *and* inter-relational approach into practice must be rooted in *patient-centered communication*: *"resonance based medicine."*

"Pain as an emotion..."

Nakamura and Chapman (2002) present a constructivist view on pain and suffering; that is, on "how pain hurts." "Classical thinking in neuroscience has characterized pain as a predominantly sensory experience... current knowledge would justify construing *pain as an emotion with sensory features as opposed to the older notion of a sensory experience with emotional sequela* [emphasis added]" (Nakamura & Chapman, 2002, p. 202). The authors summarize, "The constructivist model of pain can go beyond classical pain theory to account for the following problems: pain reflects top-down influences as well as bottom-up signaling of tissue damage; pain can exist with or without tissue damage; *pain is mainly an affective phenomenon; pain acts like an attractor in dynamical systems theory* [emphasis added]" (Nakamura & Chapman, 2002, p. 202).

The experience of pain triggers a complex set of avoidance behaviors as well as a search for assistance. Jensen (2016) thoroughly discusses the implications of two distinct neural networks—the Behavioral Activation System (BAS) and the Behavioral Inhibition System (BIS)—in trying to understand and treat chronic pain. Under the guidance of the BIS, pain is frequently used as an "admission ticket" to the interventional medical system which has a primary goal of fighting (i.e., reducing or eliminating) the pain, most often via analgesic medications ("pain killers") and/or even surgery. After years of chronification, this approach often makes the problem worse, for despite brief periods of relief achieved with biomedically focused treatments, the risk of even greater suffering and helplessness due to dependency may increase.

Neuroplasticity, i.e., changes in neural networks through learning processes on multiple levels, stabilizes an interdependent system of interacting biological, psychological, social, and spiritual factors. Such a system resists efforts to induce quick and radical changes, especially when only biological factors, such as suspected underlying nerve damage and/or tissue inflammation, are addressed. Reducing the suffering and improving the overall quality of life of the patient requires more complex bio-psycho-social interventions. Changes are needed that can provide *new* experiences. Such experiences aim at *"more of this is needed"* (i.e., treatments that activate the BAS) rather than focusing on pain as the *"only thing to get rid of"* (i.e. driving the BIS).

The conventional biomedical approach that sees the patient as a passive receiver of treatment does not allow him to cope effectively with pain, stress, and/or other related life challenges. What can be done to help patients help themselves? The important questions that arise here are: What resources are available to the patient that can help him to reduce suffering? *"What instead?"* should and could be the center of awareness, of cognition, or of behavior in order to promote self-competence, self-efficacy, and well-being? Any and all encounters of the two approaches—i.e., the one for *being* ill and the other for ill*ness*—must proceed within the context of *interactive resonance*. The character of these encounters must heighten acceptance of the fact that handing over any painful part of the body for repair is not an option.

Among other approaches, Jensen (2016) finds hypnosis appropriate, since it "could have a direct effect on creating new associations in either the BIS or BAS (depending on the specific suggestions offered) which then would facilitate the establishment of new automatic responses to pain or other stimuli" (Jensen, 2016, p. 529.e11). David Spiegel (1985), a recognized expert in the field of psycho-oncology, found hypnosis to be especially useful to "filter the hurt out of the pain," not only with cancer patients.

The Core Element of Hypnosis and "Resonance Based Medicine" is Therapeutic Communication

Communicating with the patient *in resonance* supports required changes. *Patient-centered therapeutic communication* (see Figure 1) corresponds to a pyramid of layers, one on top of the other. Translated into clinical practice, the layers of communication are, of course, not distinct. They refer here to the key aspects in communication that guide the treatment. Their effective application requires mindfulness for the fundamental law of interpersonal communication in which the *receiver's* interpretation of the communicated message, rather than the *sender's*, is considered to be decisive.

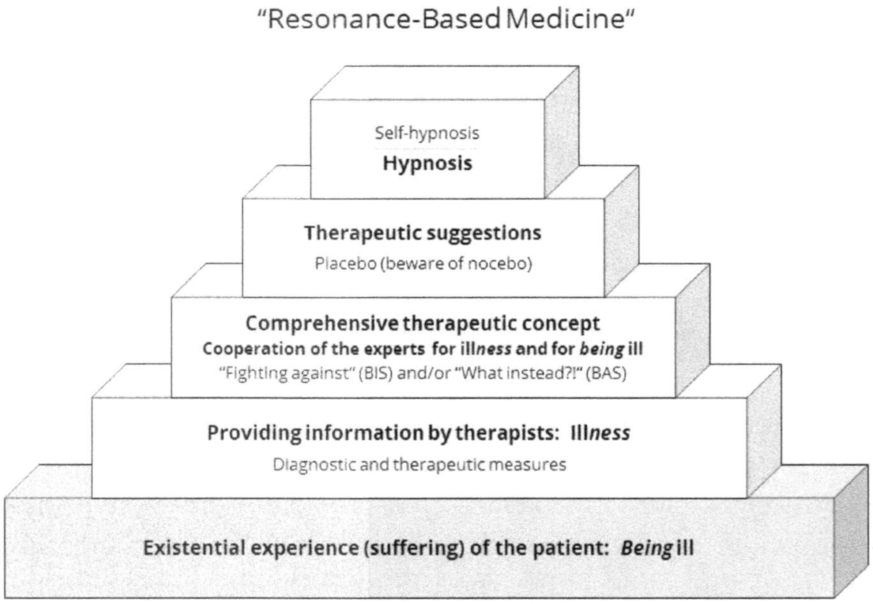

"Resonance-Based Medicine"

Self-hypnosis
Hypnosis

Therapeutic suggestions
Placebo (beware of nocebo)

Comprehensive therapeutic concept
Cooperation of the experts for ill*ness* and for *being* ill
"Fighting against" (BIS) and/or "What instead?!" (BAS)

Providing information by therapists: Ill*ness*
Diagnostic and therapeutic measures

Existential experience (suffering) of the patient: *Being* ill

Figure 12-1. Levels of communication in resonance based medicine

The patient's existential experience of *being* ill, with the concomitant suffering that necessitates medical treatment and/or therapeutic support, serves as the basis of any therapeutic communication.

With respect to the first layer, all patients need to be provided with necessary information about their ill*ness* (fulfilling the legal duty to inform and ask for consent for any treatment) in a manner that facilitates anxiety reduction (i.e., addressing the underlying question, "What's wrong with me?") and that can transmit confidence for a good outcome.

Second, and especially when dealing with chronic pain, the therapist must present himself as a collaborator who is contributing his knowledge (e.g., state-of-the-art treatment guidelines based on "evidence based medicine", Sackett et al., 1996) as an expert on ill*ness*. The patient is contributing his expertise of *being* ill, and thus is capable of determining if and when treatment goals have been or are being achieved. By taking both perspectives into account all clinical decisions can evolve *in resonance*: *"shared decision making."*

The critical role of the third layer, that approaches hypnosis, is often underestimated. Broadly based clinical research (Varga, 2011; Kekecs & Varga, 2013, Cyna et al., 2011) illustrates the power and efficacy of suggestions provided in treatment settings without formal trance induction. Clinicians can, and for the benefit of their patients indeed should in the clinical setting, make use of positive suggestions, better known as the placebo response. The clinician must be aware of a patient's readiness to accept a suggestion in order to avoid negative suggestions that may well make things worse (e.g., a surgeon making a statement such as, "You will hurt like hell when you wake up in the recovery room."; Bejenke, 1996, p. 214).

Hypnosis and self-hypnosis are not separate tools but are self-evident procedural steps in the continuity of interdependent aspects or layers of this pyramid model of *patient-centered therapeutic communication*. Positioned on top of the pyramid, as sequential measures of a development, they appear neither exotic, nor extraordinary—even when combined with a formal ritual of hypnotic induction, or when using hand levitation or other peculiar hypnotic phenomena. *Therapeutic communication* is the core element both of hypnosis itself and of a medical practice based on *intersubjective exchange in resonance*: *"resonance based medicine."*

Hypnosis and Self-Hypnosis are at the Pinnacle of a "Resonance Based Medicine" Approach to Dealing with Chronic Pain

When applied to the treatment of chronic pain, *resonance* implies using the authority of medical expertise in order to transmit the key notion to the patient that *he or she alone is the expert in regards to changes that are necessary and possible*. The clinician-patient relationship can best be seen as a joint venture that aims at catalyzing the processes of personal change, rather than delivering ready-made solutions. Its aim is to "restore or maintain the patient's sense of competence, increase the patient's sense of control, foster self-mastery and independence, enable the patient to retain dignity, include the patient as an integral and active participant in his care instead of a passive recipient" (Bejenke, 1996, p. 211). Although interventional and directive hypnotic techniques can be effective in an acute setting for pain control, chronic pain requires a cooperative effort. *Hypnosis offers a way of teaching the patient how to use self-hypnosis*.

It is of central importance to enable the patient to make a decisive transition from the problem-oriented search to fight or reduce pain (BIS), toward a solution-oriented BAS approach. Here, questions such as "How would you like to feel?" and "How should it feel instead?" invite the individual responses from the patient to answer personally with a multitude of desirable perceptions. Within the context of an atmosphere of trust, not too many steps are required to test these options by relaxing and imagining a "favorite place" where these qualities *can be experienced as real to the extent that it makes a difference to the patient.* The advantage of this approach is that any improvement referring to a valued "What instead?" goal can be perceived as progress and rewarding and is an impulse into the BAS; while a reduction of pain (as source of the suffering, BIS) is unlikely to be experienced as progress unless it gets very close to zero, which is indeed unlikely for most chronic pain patients.

It would, however, be naïve to view this approach as the simplistic proposal that in order for chronic pain to go away patients just need to think positively and practice self-hypnosis. Without an understanding and therapeutic processing of related bio-psycho-social and spiritual issues, years of suffering will allow for only limited progress. The stability of the system—i.e., the missing predisposition for easy change—is anchored in an unconscious conditioning of implicit biographical memories, helplessness, pain, physical, and/or perhaps sexual abuse. These converge in a sort of glow that generates the heat and smoke of chronic pain and suffering. Since hypnosis is conceptualized as an *intersubjective, relational exchange* (Erickson, 2013; Haley, 2015) *rather than the mere application of (yet another) powerful (but invasive) technique* it is particularly effective in addressing these supplementary and yet influential aspects of chronic pain. The intimacy of a present-day relationship that is intensely protective and trustworthy encourages in and of itself relief and overall stress reduction. Its characteristic quality of *"attunement"* (Bonshtein, 2012) that enables an adequate understanding of the patient's past experiences is a prerequisite for addressing chronic pain suffering and for exploring the patient's options for a better future.

Hypnosis can offer access to "rooms for change" (McClintock, 1999) in which associative fields containing painful memories can be processed, resolved, and/or integrated in such a way that previous experiences are no longer able to function unconsciously as "triggers" for stress and pain. When past incidents are no longer the designated problem, today's peace can be made with what happened in the past. Even if the traces left by such incidents in the patient's memories are the cause of trouble, what happened in the past cannot be changed. The memory of the past, however, can be changed; neuroplasticity is gospel for the rehabilitation of chronic pain patients, even though, paradoxically, it acts as the basis of chronification as well.

Hypnotic and self-hypnotic imagination of an adaptive "What instead?" and being in a "safe place" (visual, auditory, kinesthetic, olfactory, gustatory) can facilitate the experience of feeling comfortably and entirely secure—especially when there are many reasons for feeling bad and endangered by conditions that may not disappear "just like that" (e.g., cancer treatment or being chronically ill). The experiences of feeling secure within oneself serve as a sort of power station; where the batteries of personal confidence can be recharged in order to be able to meet up with and to fulfill the requirements and the challenges of everyday life.

The patience, confidence, and nurturing quality of a patient-therapist relationship *in resonance* encourage the patient to make his or her own choices. This benign *intersubjective resonance* between persons serves as a model and as a source of induction for the restoration of a better *intrapersonal resonance* of the individual patient that emanates from homeostatic regulation (Brown, 1991). This too facilitates change in the patient's relationship with pain.

Change and Healing:
A Hypnosystemic Approach
to Chronification and Rehabilitation

Resonance (Rosa, 2016; Ebell, 2017) indicates a professionally shaped sphere of relatedness as a process of mutual influence during a collaborative effort to identify possibilities of change. Seen from a systems perspective, even a problem depicted as the *worst*—including the subjective experience of pain and suffering—represents the best possible solution for the individual *under the given conditions*. Any therapeutic impulse to target a better solution requires a "comprehensive treatment concept operating on three major operational levels simultaneously: intrapersonal, interactional, and contextual" (Ebell, 1995, p. 4).

In terms of its function according to systems theory, chronic pain acts as an "attractor," as well as an "attention-getter," in its ability to invoke the conscious awareness of the person concerned. This insures the high intrinsic stability of the system. In contrast, the subjective experience of pain invokes an absolute need for change and a maximum activation of the BIS. Chapman et al. (2008) explain that, "the nervous-endocrine-immune ensemble constitutes a single overarching system, or supersystem, that responds as a whole to tissue trauma and contributes to the multidimensional subjective experience of pain. This leads to the hypothesis that supersystem dysregulation contributes significantly to chronic pain and related multisymptom disorders" (Chapman et al., p. 123). They go on to say, "Supersystem dysregulation (is) prolonged dysfunction in the ability of a system to recover its normal relationship to other systems and its normal level of operation after perturbation" (Chapman et al., p. 135).

The primary task and challenge is thus to *constructively destabilize the status quo of the system in order to induce change for the better.* This goal is achieved by (1) identifying the patient's resources for experimentation with something that could open a door to positive experiences and by (2) identifying (auto-) suggestions that by continuously activating the BAS augment a personal counterbalance to pain and suffering. The aim here is not only to induce *"first order" quantitative* changes (e.g., reduction of pain intensity and/or quality) but *"second order" qualitative* changes in the patient's perception and overall quality of life as well. Progress (healing) is tantamount to the emergence of a complex system and cannot be fabricated and/or controlled completely in the therapeutic exchange of the partners. Change happens.

Any search for appropriate hypnotic (auto-)suggestions is facilitated by ideomotor signaling (Cheek, 1994). This technique allows the clinician and the patient to determine if proposed suggestions are consistent with the patient's inner values and experiences, and for the patient to disclose ambivalence and/or a variety of different views. Just like a traffic light that provides the driver with a green (go!), red (stop!), or orange (proceed with caution!) guidance, ideomotor signaling indicates how to best proceed, especially when discussions on a cognitive level tend to confuse and cause uncertainty.

Case Report:
Complex Regional Pain Syndrome

My treatment of a patient with a 10-year history of Complex Regional Pain Syndrome (CRPS) can serve here as an illustration of *collaborating in resonance* within the framework of a *comprehensive therapeutic concept*. This syndrome is characterized by a high degree of suffering due to pain and the disabled state of the involved extremity and its dramatic tendency toward deterioration. Exacerbations can be triggered by normal physical activities and by emotional stress. This very special dysregulation of a normally reliable healing process (underlying an overreaction and/or lacking inhibition of inflammatory cascades in the neuro-endocrine system) was first described in the beginning of the last century by the surgeon Paul Sudeck, and, until recently, CRPS was also labeled "Sudeck's dystrophy"(Agarwal-Kozlowski et al., 2011; Sudeck, 1900).

Looking back on her "career" of being a chronic pain patient, Mrs. T, 55 years old, is convinced that psychotherapy, hypnosis, and self-hypnosis helped her to learn to live decisively with her pain in general, to reduce her suffering, and to become an appreciated and equal decision-making partner. All of this was done in order to optimize her medical treatment in regards to the quality and intensity of rehabilitation exercises, the handling of analgesic opiate-medication, and the use of invasive medical procedures like botox-injections, infusions, etc. from time to time.

A Small Path of Worrying Develops into a Highway of Pain and Suffering

Mrs. T's problem began after an arthroscopy of the right elbow joint and the suture of a tendon. She developed typical CRPS symptoms in her right hand, which, despite immediate recognition and treatment of the syndrome, not only persisted but changed for the worse; this was disastrous for the right-handed homemaker who also worked as a secretary. It was only after three years of deterioration that she was adequately treated in an interdisciplinary and multimodal hospital setting with a clear recommendation for continuous ambulatory psychotherapeutic treatment of the concomitant depressive reaction.

In a first phase of collaboration we focused on identifying those factors that induced feelings of emotional overload in her relationships at home and at work, and we explored how these feelings could be managed more effectively. Emotional reactions, (mostly feelings of being "moved") and tears, surprised her, as did her cognitive associations to traumatizing past events.

The working hypothesis for our collaborative research as experts for ill*ness* and *being* ill was the following personification of "Mr. Sudeck," i.e., her pain-problem. What if he were an extremely demanding and rigid teacher rather than the cruel torturer she experienced at the outset of treatment. As a teacher, he uses draconian punishment and offers no explanation as to "why" he overreacts to any level of physical or emotional stress. What if a part of herself (i.e., her own strictness) is as judgmental and merciless as Mr. Sudeck is? This is an old fashioned, fundamentalist, educational method of disciplinary punishment that does not allow for a single mistake and prohibits normalcy and healing.

Mr. Sudeck's pedagogic style is, without the slightest doubt, unacceptable, and it maximally activates her BIS. There is, however, a big "but," for he might in fact be well-meaning. If she is able to receive the messages he is trying to convey and she can make progress in developing more effective coping strategies, he may turn out to be just a strict teacher who does not accept cheating. Given Mrs. T's strong sense of duty and discipline, Mr. Sudeck is in truth aware of stressors long before Mrs. T, herself, would notice. Actually, Mr. Sudeck might, in the long run, help her discover how to reduce her overall stress, which could eventually help her to achieve a better quality of life in general.

The most difficult part for us both as experts for ill*ness* and *being* ill was to not put blame on anyone or anything, but instead to use her insights pragmatically in order to strengthen her BAS. From this point of view, Mr. Sudeck proved to be a reliable and knowledgeable investigator who evaluated intrapersonal, interpersonal, and contextual changes thoroughly.

On the other hand, his tendency to overreact and to use pain intensity as punishment was not useful feedback. A more gentle reaction on his side would help her to experiment more with the "what instead" approach and to generate more and more positive experiences (BAS); achieving a better quality of life or even healing. Mr. Sudeck's retirement became our shared goal, i.e., that Mrs. T could be more accepting and more merciful with herself. If she were to acquire the self-competence and self-efficacy needed in order to take care of herself, well, Mr. Sudeck would no longer have to be so fiercely vigilant and suspicious of her anymore.

Within two years a certain level of acceptance was attained. Mrs. T understood that Mr. Sudeck (i.e., the pain), other symptoms, and specific reactions represented only one of many aspects of herself as a complex system and that her CRPS was not a weird, external, malevolent energy that was bullying her. A vital part of this learning process was the need to work through and finally overcome her own attitude that her right arm was the *only* problem ("If I didn't have this d#&! CRPS, everything would be alright!"). Her first coping strategy had been the attempt to ignore it ("The right hand does not belong to me"). However, since her arm hurt so much the strategy was ineffective and proved useless. As a consequence, she cursed her "f&%!ing hand," and for some months even searched for a surgeon who would be willing to amputate it. We eventually found the following "what instead": *"My hand belongs to me, and it is my duty and job to care for it, even when or especially, because it is such a trouble maker."*

Mrs. T reduced her work hours, practiced saying "No," and gave the requests of her family members and her colleagues careful thought before automatically answering "Yes, I'll take care of that." Her ongoing opiate medication regimen, which, prior to psychotherapeutic treatment had not resulted in adequate palliation, began to provide sufficient pain relief. She learned to take time to care for herself through rest, sports activities, and relaxation in self-hypnosis. After 22 treatment sessions Mrs. T decided it was no longer necessary to continue her psychotherapy.

Two-and-a-half years later I received an email with an update on her medical status and her ups and downs. Just before she wrote she had, all by herself, withdrawn from a regimen of very high dose fentanyl. In her email she posed the following question: "I was able to control my pain pretty well until recently, but now the muscle tonus in my arm is so high that I am unable to open my hand any more. I have been wearing a brace on the hand for about a year, but it feels as if my hand and forearm are torn apart. I think that that's why my pain is getting worse and harder to control. Do you think it would make sense to try self-hypnosis?" My immediate answer was, "Yes, I do." She then came back to see me for self-hypnosis training.

Transcript (Hypnosis Session)

After an in-depth review of the course of her pain therapy and her coping strategies in the time since our last session two years ago, and after discussing relevant changes in her personal and professional relationship systems, we focused on Mrs. T's formulation of her primary treatment goal. Although proud of having been able to maintain her pain in general to a level of about 4 (measured by a numerical rating scale from 0 to 10), she hoped to learn the necessary skills in order to effectively relax her affected arm and shoulder and to reestablish an awareness of the forearm as the natural anatomic connection between the elbow and the hand.

Clinician: Mrs. T, we have talked in detail about your problems for about an hour. So let's turn to an in-depth discussion of a suitable "What instead?" Let's concentrate on developing ideas that could help you to be better able to relax your arm and your shoulder, and especially, what could be an alternative sensation for your hand and forearm, which have felt somehow torn apart for quite a while now.

[I use her own wording of the problem while I turn to consideration of a possible solution, i.e., her personal alternative and individual "What instead?"]

What would be your number-one wish on your priority wishlist today if your unconscious mind would be able to fulfill it, just like that?

Patient: I want to regain a feeling that the arm is, in itself complete, so that I'll be able to let go and relax it more easily as a whole. I remember something a doctor in Sri Lanka said last year. I contacted him during a vacation there, and he told me that I am blocked, that there are many blockades, and that it is necessary to achieve a flow again.

Clinician: Do you feel a blockade right now? And if so, where?

Patient: When I turn my attention to my right shoulder and arm now—I usually try to avoid being aware of them at all, much less to focus on how they feel—my perception ends at the elbow. Then there is a gap, and my perception starts again in my fingers.

Clinician: Would you mind closing your eyes and telling me what you see between your elbow and your fingers?

[More a suggestion than a question.]

Patient: *[After a pause.]* I see something like the image from an accident. Something anatomical. Just bone and flesh; each end torn apart and frayed.

Clinician: Sounds like an understandable reason for feeling pain and for suffering.

Patient: That picture scares me. It looks icky, disgusting.

Clinician: Remember how we successfully collaborated years ago on overcoming your fantasy of tearing the arm out? You had developed that fantasy as an attempt to get rid of the pain and the other problems in your hand.

If you had torn out the arm back then, it might have looked like that. But focus *now* on what might be the alternative to such an icky and disgusting picture of an arm torn into pieces with frayed ends. What comes to your mind, when you concentrate *now* on an image and/or a feeling of how it should and could look and feel like instead?

Maybe you have to think about it… or maybe it'll develop just by itself and get clearer and clearer… just take your time, lean back with your head resting on your shoulders, and your arms resting on your thighs…. Take a few deep breaths, and relax... and just wait a little for what is going to happen.

Patient: [*After some minutes.*] **A thought, a sentence comes up: "It is going to be whole again!"**

Clinician: [*Assuring.*] **This seems perfect. If it is fitting for you and your unconscious mind, you can relax deeper and deeper... and feel more and more comfortable... to discover what your arm needs. What *you* need, and what may help the *two ends to start to come together and to heal and to become a whole again,* and what is necessary and helpful *to let them grow together again and heal to become a whole again.***

The *deeper* you float into a feeling of deep confidence... that this might not only be possible but that it will happen—even after so many years of pain and suffering—the *lighter* the other hand will feel. Your left hand will show you and me that your unconscious is willing... will cooperate... to support this project of yours of healing, by feeling lighter and lighter.

The signal may be to lift just a little bit from its position of lying comfortably on your thigh because it feels lighter and lighter, whereas the rest of your body feels comfortably heavy and relaxed. If this is going to happen, if your number-one wish is going to be answered and fulfilled, then *it'll happen all by itself, just like the healing of tissue is something happening all by itself.* If there is flow again where there have been blockades, these blockades can and will be resolved.

[With minimal hesitating, jerky movements her left hand rises several inches, as if it were driven by a geared wheel, typical of ideomotor movements. To my surprise there is a

similar movement in the fingers of her right hand too. They
spread a little and lift up from the brace, visible, since the
tape on the brace only covers the knuckles. Mrs. T seems
calm, her breathing is deep and regular, her eyes are moving
behind her eyelids.]

If you are feeling alright now, I suppose you are taking the
first steps on your new path to healing. Maybe an
experience will emerge that can lead you along this path, an
experience made up of what you feel, see, hear, and maybe
even taste. Ideally, it will consist of all of the elements you
need for healing, and it may become an ideal basis for your
self-hypnosis exercises, the reason why you contacted me
again, after years of very successfully coping with the strain
of pain and stress of your everyday pressure and challenges.

Patient: I can see and feel a pipe, much like my brace. It is
round and it encloses my forearm, protecting it, from the
elbow to the knuckles of my hand. I can't look through it;
because it is sort of metallic. I can't see what happens in
there.

Clinician: Could there be something else in there other than
your arm, in the pipe, something helpful that will *optimize*
the healing of both ends and help to connect them to become a
whole again?

Patient: Chamomile flowers, something natural to support
healing.

Clinician: A powerful remedy, well known since ancient
times. ... Is something else in there, in the pipe, to support
healing?

Patient: *[Reporting with eyelids still closed.]* That's interesting;
the metal pipe is changing into something else. Now it's a

kind of bark, the bark of a tree; a bark that has many outer and inner layers. The inner layers are responsible for growth and nurturing of the trunk, the outer for protecting it. ... I think it is a birch tree. I love birch trees. I see them very often when I go for a walk where I live. It is surrounded by a marsh.

Clinician: That sounds perfect. Just sink into this experience *as deeply as possible now* by taking another deep breath. You and your unconscious, I think, are doing a great job. Just watch now, if anything else is going to happen to help you to generate the ideal idea of regeneration. You have all the time you need—[*Voice lowered, to emphasize the post-hypnotic suggestion*]—*to store this strong healing image in your memory, so you can call on it again, ask it to appear again during your self-hypnosis practice as vividly as it is right now to support you and your healing project*—[*Voice as before*] although it'll be just a few minutes in real time.

As long as your left hand is still floating, I suppose that this is the time you need for letting everything that is helpful sink into your memory, into the archives. In these archives there are memories that might be waiting, ready to show up, when they are needed, and some parts are better sealed, so that they don't bother you anymore. And there is a wise archivist who knows what belongs to which part of the archive.

[*Indirect suggestion for amnesia for the feeling of the arm as if torn apart and for a quick recall of her pipe of birch bark imagination of healing.*]

Healing makes a difference right from the beginning... and especially in the long run. You certainly know and remember the potential of the body to heal wounds; such as a cut in the skin. It happens all by itself, sometimes with scars that are difficult to see, even if you look for them with a magnifying lens.

Patient: [*Appearing very calm, facial muscles relaxed, breathing regularly, her left hand lowering very slowly, inch by inch, as if driven by a geared wheel.*]

Clinician: [*Reorientation.*] As soon as the fingertips of your left hand touch your thigh again, your hand will come to rest. It'll feel normal again and it doesn't have to signal anything to anybody anymore. It's just your left hand with its own weight; it can function normally and as needed. The contact of hand and thigh will be the starting point for you to count back silently from 10 to 0, number by number, step by step, to say goodbye to the inner world, your healing image, and to promise to return from time to time during self-hypnosis as discussed. ... At about 5, half-way back to the here and now of sitting comfortably in this chair here in my office, you take a deep breath... and when you arrive at 0, you'll open your eyes, look around, stretch your arms and legs and be fully oriented.

Patient: [*After a while, smiling.*] I didn't expect that. The last thing that I saw was a normal elbow and forearm as a whole; no torn ends anymore!

Clinician: Congratulations. Looks like a good start. We'll discuss your experiences with self-hypnosis by mail and soon we can have another session to support your healing project. You may use your familiar relaxation ritual for inducing self-hypnosis to focus on the image of the pipe of birch bark around your forearm. Maybe some additional images with the same healing quality will emerge, having the quality of a distinct "What instead?" compared with where we started today at the beginning of our session.

Follow-up

Starting with this session, and for the past three years, we have remained in contact. We have had several sessions, often with months in between them; during this time, Mrs. T had ups and downs. For about half a year after the described hypnosis experience she intensively practiced the healing image of a pipe of birch bark around her right forearm. Her ability to use this imagery depended on her overall stress level, but she continued to use self-hypnosis regularly for relaxation and recovery. Mrs. T is still wearing her brace for protection, and her right hand is still completely unusable for household chores. Her hand reacts with growing pain in any active exercise treatment that is necessary to prevent further deficits.

She ultimately quit her job and retired. This, as well as the death of her father the same year and the concomitant neediness of her elderly mother, induced a crisis. Her supportive husband is a continuous and present resource; they spend as much time together as possible. Pain has not ceased and it remains her major challenge. Nonetheless, in my view, the hypnotic experience described above signified a decisive step and was a turning point in the right direction; that is, to *awaken her empathy and accept her responsibility for taking care of her poor arm and hand*. Mrs. T had been an active partner as the decisive expert for her *being* ill to cooperate with professional CRPS experts in the context of a *comprehensive therapeutic concept*. Self-hypnosis serves her as reliable source of support in dealing with multiple aspects of coping with stress, pain, and with her handicapped arm.

Summary and Conclusion

To treat and manage chronic illness, especially chronic pain, *therapists and patients must join forces in a collaborative effort to seek out potential changes* in the context of an *interdisciplinary and multimodal comprehensive therapeutic concept.* This joint venture corresponds to a process of mutual learning. It is conducted in an atmosphere of *intersubjective resonance*—that is, the relatedness of two individual human beings in the roles of therapist and patient. Both act as experts of their respective perspectives; the professional for the diagnosed ill*ness* and patient for *being* ill. A prerequisite for a *therapeutic alliance* requires that their exchange be shaped professionally as a *patient-centered therapeutic communication.* Although objective and subjective limitations exist, both experts learn together where those limitations are. Well-established medical interventions based on empirical evidence ("evidence based medicine") need to be supplemented by this approach of *resonance based medicine.*

Hypnosis may offer access to resources for change and hidden potentials, and self-hypnosis may become a decisive coping strategy. Optimally tailored (auto-)suggestions are identified by analyzing the problem mutually (i.e., the patient's symptoms that act as trigger of the *Behavioral Inhibition System*) and then guiding the patient towards individual solutions that have a distinct *"What instead?!"* quality. *Ideomotor signaling* may assist this process, helping to identify appropriate goals that strengthen the *Behavioral Activation System.*

References

Agarwal-Kozlowski, K., Schumacher, T., Goerig, M., & Beck, H. (2011). Vom Morbus Sudeck zum komplexen regionalen Schmerzsyndrom (From Morbus Sudeck to complex regional pain syndrome). *Schmerz, 25,* 140-147.

Bejenke, C. (1996). Painful medical procedures. In J. Barber (Ed.), *Hypnosis and suggestion in the treatment of pain: A clinical guide* (pp. 209-266). New York, NY: Norton.

Bonshtein, U. (2012). Relational hypnosis. *International Journal of Clinical and Experimental Hypnosis, 60,* 397-415.

Brown, P. (1991). *The hypnotic brain: Hypnotherapy and social communication.* New Haven, CT: Yale University Press.

Chapman, C. R., Tuckett, R. P., & Song, C. W. (2008). Pain and stress in a systems perspective: Reciprocal neural, endocrine, and immune interactions. *Journal of Pain, 9,* 122-145.

Cheek, D. B. (1994). *Hypnosis: The application of ideomotor techniques.* Boston, MA: Allyn and Bacon.

Cyna, A. M., Andrew, M.I., Tan, S. G. M., & Smith, A .F. (2011). *Handbook of communication in anesthesia and critical care: A practical guide to exploring the art.* New York, NY: Oxford University Press.

Ebell, H. (1995). Hypnosis and cancer pain: Ericksonian approach vs. standardized suggestibility testing. In S. Lankton (Ed.), *Ericksonian monographs, No. 11, Difficult contexts in therapy* (pp. 1-8). New York, NY: Brunner and Mazel.

Ebell, H. (2017). Hypno-therapeutische Kommunikation: Kernelement einer auf Resonanz basierten Medizin [Resonance Based Medicine]. *Hypnose ZHH, 12,* 173-202.

Erickson, B. A. (2013, November) citing her father, M. H. Erickson: *Hypnosis isn't something done to someone, rather therapist and client together enter a relational field, where the conscious awareness and the unconscious of two persons are connected.* Talk presented at the Annual Congress of the

German Society of Hypnosis and Hypnotherapy, Bad Lippspringe, Germany.

Haley, J. (2015). An interactional explanation of hypnosis. *International Journal of Clinical and Experimental Hypnosis, 63,* 422-443. (first published 1958 in the *American Journal of Clinical Hypnosis, 1,* 41-57).

Jensen, M. P. (2016). The behavioral activation and inhibition systems: Implications for understanding and treating chronic pain. *Journal of Pain, 17,* 529.e1-529.e18

Kekecs, Z., & Varga, K. (2013). Positive suggestion techniques in somatic medicine: A review of the empirical studies. *Interventional Medicine & Applied Science, 5,* 101-111.

McClintock, E. (1999). *Room for change: Empowering possibilities for therapists and clients.* Needham Heights, MA: Allyn and Bacon.

Nakamura, Y., & Chapman C. R. (2002). Constructing pain: How pain hurts. In K. Yasue. M. Jibu, & T. D. Senta (Eds.), *No matter, never mind* (pp. 193-205). Amsterdam, The Netherlands: John Benjamins Publishing Company.

Rosa, H. (2016). *Resonanz: Eine Soziologie der Weltbeziehung.* Berlin, Germany: Suhrkamp.

Sackett, D., Rosenberg, W., Gray, M., Haynes, B., & Richardson, S. (1996). Evidence based medicine: What it is and what it isn't. *British Medical Journal, 312,* 71-72.

Sauerbruch, F., & Wenke, H. (1936). *Wesen und Bedeutung des Schmerzes.* Berlin, Germany: Junker und Dünnhaupt.

Sudeck, P. (1900). Über die akute entzündliche Knochenatrophie. *Archiv für Klinishe Chirurgie, 62,* 147-156.

Varga, K. (2011). *Beyond the words: Communication and suggestion in medical practice.* New York, NY: Nova Science Publishers.

CHAPTER 13

The Pain Switch for Teens
with Complex Pain

Leora Kuttner

Pain comes naturally—so can relief!

Leora Kuttner is a Clinical Psychologist, Clinical Professor of Pediatrics at University of British Columbia and BC Children's Hospital, Vancouver, and is a documentary filmmaker. She pioneered work in pediatric pain relief using psychophysiological methods—particularly hypnosis—and has taught these methods throughout Europe, the Middle East, Australia, Canada, and the US for over 35 years. Dr. Kuttner has published many professional articles and wrote the books, A Child in Pain: How to Help, What to Do, *and* A Child in Pain: What Health Professionals Can Do to Help. *In 1985, Dr. Kuttner directed the award-winning film* No Fears, No Tears, *and in 1998 she directed its sequel,* No Fears, No Tears—13 Years Later, *documenting how children with cancer benefit from hypnosis. In 2003, she created* Making Every Moment Count, *a documentary about pediatric palliative care with The National Film Board of Canada, and in 2013 she created,* Dancing with Pain, *a film exploring teens with chronic pain.*

She won the "The Woman of Distinction" honor in Vancouver, the Outstanding Alumni for Professional Achievement award from Simon Fraser University, the American Pain Society's Jeffrey Lawson Award for Advocacy for Children's Pain Relief, and the William C. Wester Award for Excellence in Child Hypnosis from the American Society of Clinical Hypnosis. She is Vice-President of the Canadian Society of Clinical Hypnosis (BC Division), faculty with the National Pediatric Hypnosis Training Institute, and is in practice treating children and teens—using hypnosis all the time!

* * *

Finding ways to successfully treat pain has been my life-long fascination. Hypnosis provides the language and flexibility—indeed a comprehensive approach—to address this complex condition. Pain is more than a negative sensory signal; it's a culturally influenced, learned, psychophysiological emotional experience.

Many areas of the brain are involved in learning, over time, to coordinate within fractions of seconds in order to assess and make sense of the signal as "pain." To do this, our brain rapidly accesses previous experiences in memory to recall similar signals, then evaluates its intensity, and determines the meaning of this particular sensory input.

The process is fairly straightforward with short-term or acute pain; however, this is not the case with persistent or chronic pain. When many previous and varied experiences are layered upon each other, this interpretative process, predetermined by a longer history of pain occurrences, results in the pain-brain networks becoming more rigid, predictable, and less open to change. The neutral sensory signal then becomes intertwined with distress, frustration, repeated disappointments, and failures to manage or reduce the pain, thereby escalating feelings of despair, isolation, anxiety, and/or depression.

Hypnosis is a natural and elegant fit with the unique problems of treating persistent pain. Hypnosis is communication; verbal and nonverbal, conscious and subconscious. This communication occurs not only in what is being said, but also in what is implied between the words, by how the words are delivered, and in the silence. Our careful and deliberate selection of language to create a climate of new possibilities from the moment of first contact with a patient is fundamental to achieving pain relief.

The hypnotic experience invites multiple aspects of experience to occur and change simultaneously or sequentially; that is, to think *differently* about this experience, to focus attention moment by moment on beneficial shifts in feelings and physical experiences, and thus to develop new patterns of pain processing and new neurobiological networks.

There remains a tendency to diagnose pain conditions using out-dated dichotomies; in particular, that pain is either psychogenic-functional or physical-organic, implying that the source of the problem resides either in the mind or in the body. Today, scientific evidence strongly indicates that persisting or chronic pain is an entire mind-body, integrated nervous system dysfunction (Melzack, 1999; Woolf, 2011).

Hypnosis has the striking advantage of being able to address the pain experience simultaneously at sensory, cognitive, and affective-emotion levels, while the patient is in a relaxed, receptive, physical state (Jensen, 2009; Wood & Bioy, 2008). This facilitates the development of a very different relationship with the pain. Few other therapies address as much at one time.

The Set-up:
Utilizing Naturalistic Hypnosis

Teens in ongoing, persistent, or complex pain are notoriously intolerant of "yet another consultation about my pain." They've had clinicians tell them, "There's nothing more we can do," or, "We found nothing on your tests, so you'll just have to learn to live with it." Engaging a disheartened, listless teen requires ingenuity, perceptive responses, and humour—but only in the right place. Being authentic and creating rapport is central.

However, considerable information/explanation is also required in the first session to frame the patient's understanding of how pain works and why the brain and brain processes are so important in this therapeutic endeavour. Gathering her (two-thirds of teens referred for chronic pain are female) history, establishing rapport, and providing a common foundation of understanding, while weaving the hypnotic language of possibilities and suggestions into our discussion, can create a more receptive climate.

We know in hypnosis practice that words convey meaning and multiple messages. The common diagnostic term "chronic" carries a negative load. Chronic originates from the Greek term "Chronos" meaning "pertaining to time." In today's medical use, "chronic" means a disease or condition that "persists in time."

When used as an adjective for pain, this suggests that a painful sensation is unchangeable and will persist over time. It is a dismal and dooming term, and teens are affected by it. Addressing this obstacle at the start of a pain consultation provides a point of surprise and potential re-frame for a 16-year-old patient who listlessly enters my consulting room, clearly not happy to be here. She has been given a pain diagnosis of "central sensitization disorder" and says to me:

Patient: I have chronic pain.

Clinician: It's only chronic until it changes, then it's not!

[I've got her attention.]

...because it's very possible for you to become the boss of your pain, instead of the other way around.

[Teens with persistent pain tire and resent telling "their story" to the multiple clinicians that they are sent to consult with. I've found it crucial to start the session with something different—and in this case, a new frame of understanding. Sound research demonstrates that pain can be modulated and changed over time (Jensen, 2009; Wood & Bioy, 2008). In the first session, I share this evidence with diagrams emphasizing the recognized plasticity of our nervous system.]

Clinician: You, of course know, that our brains are designed to learn!

Patient: *[She gives a small nod to this statement of fact.]*

[What follows is naturalistic or informal hypnosis, to build rapport with a very cautious, fearful teen and to create a climate of change.]

Clinician: Well, this applies to our entire nervous system, including the brain and the body. We are designed to learn and adapt. With new experiences, like that of noticing some easing as you settle into the couch, our nervous system shifts, becoming more malleable, learning how to achieve and maintain what is beneficial.

Patient: *[She nods with uncertainty.]*

Clinician: With practice, one can go back to this state and place of easing, again and again... and in so doing can create new patterns, new reliable networks that sustain your comfort and relief. Other teens have experienced this process, often at first feeling a little unsure yet hoping, dearly, for a way through the pain. I wonder how intrigued you'll become when you notice small and then significant changes happening... how curious you'll be about how much it can be different for you.

> [She's quite hesitant, which is not uncommon in teens with a history of persistent pain.]

The fascinating finding is that we have the built-in capacity to re-sprout neuronal networks and the more these networks are used to create comfort, the stronger these networks develop.

> [Piquing her curiosity with suggestions builds a therapeutic web to begin to indirectly nudge away or dislodge her despair, anxiety, or negative beliefs. Now I provide a new frame for understanding pain to address previous inadequate explanations and provide a rationale for hope.]

There are some fascinating scientific facts about pain that are important for you to know. Did you know that throughout our brain and body we have switching or gating options that control the amount of signal input to the brain?

Two scientists, Canadian, Dr. Melzack and British, Dr. Wall, researched this capacity in our peripheral and central nerves, they called this "gate control" (Melzack & Wall, 1965). We have ascending and descending pathways into the spinal cord and the brain—but it is ultimately our brain that has the major say in how much we feel... and how much it bothers us. And our brains are brilliant at learning, decoding, making sense, and interpreting signals so that we stay safe.

[She has become quietly absorbed, still in her focus; the last step in the set-up is for her to experience directly how shifting her focussed attention alters physical sensation.]

Clinician: May I touch your arm?

Patient: Okay.

[I gently tap her arm.]

Clinician: What kind of touch was that?

Patient: A little tap.

Clinician: Now I'm going to touch you differently. *[I stroke her arm with forefinger.]* Which do you prefer?

Patient: The second one.

Clinician: Good! See how quickly you were able to access the memory of the first signal in your brain and compare it with the second signal—and in a flash to know which signal you prefer. Now, as I continue to stroke your arm, listen to that bus passing. Track it with all your focus and attention and let me know when it's gone.

Patient: *[She shifts her attention and is quiet for a few seconds, then nods.]* It's gone.

Clinician: Was the sensation stronger or weaker when your attention was on the bus?

Patient: It felt kind of faint.

Clinician: That's right! That is the power of *your brain to select what you wish* to focus on. Then what you focus on becomes more important than anything else, and the less relevant signal, this boring touch, becomes faint. Tracking that bus was more important.

Patient: *[Smiles.]*

> *[By inviting her to experience a benign sensation with some curiosity and no distress and then to discern what it is and which sensation she prefers, softens her guarded physical protectiveness. This prepares her to experience a shift in pain perception when her attention is shortly absorbed in a more important task, using her "pain switch."]*

But I wake up sore and the pain is with me all the time. I don't get it!

> *[She needs to better understand what has gone wrong that is causing her to be experiencing pain. Many patients with chronic pain spend years searching fruitlessly for a diagnosis. It's a dishearteningly exhausting process that rarely turns up anything organic. This aspect needs to be woven into the rationale for our hypnotic work, otherwise the hypnotic intervention will not be sustained.]*

Clinician: Now you do know—don't you—that the X-rays and medical investigations confirmed that you do not have a disease or any other nasty condition. *[She nods.]* In fact, the results show that apart from pain, you have a very healthy body.

What has happened though, is that your pain system has been turned up. The pain-brain system has become sensitized, so that body signals that were previously ignored are now being felt and interpreted as pain—as if there's something wrong... which we now know is not the case. So, the problem is how your pain system works, particularly how your brain is picking up and making sense of these sensations... *[She looks sombre and attentively at me.]* and that's what a diagnosis of central sensitization means.

So, it's now time for you to have a way to access your smart brain and begin to re-pattern and turn that sensitized pain system... down... way down. With practice, when you turn down the discomforting sensation so that it bothers you less and less, you retrain your pain system to be bothered less and less... and to re-pattern to feel comfort, which always seeps in once the bother is gone. How is that for you?

Patient: Is it difficult? That sounds kind of hard...

[She's become more receptive. It's time to bridge to formal hypnosis of the "Pain Switch" through questions to reduce her apprehension and heighten her motivation.]

Clinician: You know of course that our brains and our bodies are designed to learn, change, and adapt.

[General truism to which she readily nods in agreement.]

Isn't it good to now know that you can access this by deliberately focussing your attention on what you want to change?

[A question that moves a step closer to her as an individual to foster her motivation and relate the general information to our therapeutic plan. She says "Yes" after a slight hesitation, revealing her doubts after two years of being in pain.]

[Slowing down and pacing my delivery.] And most important... having had this tough pain for two years, the more you experience using your smart brain, focusing your attention to closing gates, or to shift down switches, the stronger your networks become at creating and maintaining a soothed and calmer body. This becomes your new normal... each time

you down-modulate *[modulating my voice down]* **the discomfort in your body to experience more and more ease and comfort, the more the feeling of comfort increases. It's what you're designed for, the learning takes hold and your confidence grows.**

> *[Stated as a goal, but in how this is expressed this statement becomes the first of many hypnotic suggestions that create a readiness and rationale for our work together. The repetition of the word "more" provides a soothing hypnotic movement, inviting the fulfillment of why she came for help.*
>
> *Disheartened teens with chronic pain do not engage unless the process becomes personally relevant and makes sense. They roll their eyes or grudgingly remain with obvious disinterest. To create the right climate of change, I join; making her goal explicitly our goal. This creates a pathway for hope to enter. Hope is a subtle and critical component for pain relief.]*

Because you've come here in order to feel and get better.

Patient: *[Nods her head and tears up with feelings of helplessness, sadness, and despair and begins to cry. She's now freely expressing the pent-up emotional and physical tension that accompanies long-held pain, distress, and hopelessness.]*

Clinician: You've had a really rough time…

Patient: I can't do what I love. It's hard to leave the house as I don't know how I'll manage outside… at school or with my friends… anyway, I have to see so many doctors and no one has helped me.

Clinician: Would you be willing to learn a technique that draws on what you've learned today… one that empowers you to be the boss of your own body?… and gives you back

some control over your sensations, so that you can start feeling better?

Patient: *[Strongly nods her head through her tears and says with frustration...]* That's what I want—more control over my life!

Clinician: I can help you to help yourself, and you'll be so interested in how empowering the process becomes.... You dearly want more control over your life and a better relationship with your body... you are now ready to experience the Pain Switch!

Formal Hypnosis: The Pain Switch

Of the many hypnosis techniques developed to create analgesia (Barber & Adrian, 1982), one of my favorites that I've relied on is the Pain Switch; it's deceptively simple and direct. Overtly targeting the intensity of the pain experience, it simultaneously develops coping and self-management skills. Used over time, this technique facilitates a less fear-laden and more neutral relationship with pain. It is also easy to adapt to all ages. With younger teens or children, language needs to be developmentally adjusted (Kohen & Olness, 2011) using simpler words, shorter sentences, and a more dynamic delivery—all tailored to the child's age, stage, and concerns.

In the section that follows, my 16-year-old teen is guided into how to access and down-modulate her pain using the Pain Switch.

Clinician: Remember the diagram, how the brain receives all signals from your body... then interprets them, creating your experience through the descending pathways to your body? Now let's access those brain sites so you can begin to down-modulate those signals so that they bother you less and less.

[I previously introduced the more tolerable term "bother" as a step-down from her previous heightened distress. By tagging it now with "down-modulate" both her distress and her new understanding of pain are simultaneously addressed.]

Patient: *[Is now focussing completely on me. Her tears stop and she nods quietly.]*

[Therapeutically, I intend to tightly integrate physical, emotional, and mental into a hypnotic change experience. The more she processes while she simultaneously addresses her emotional distress, her troubling beliefs, and her physical pain, the quicker she'll absorb this as her first step in a more adaptive way of coping.

[Note, this is not CBT; the interaction isn't at a rational conscious level but rather occurs in a naturalistic altered state of consciousness.]

Clinician: That's right... on the next breath out, notice how your eyes seem to have a mind of their own and automatically close when they're ready... that's it!

Patient: *[Her eyes close. She settles herself more comfortably into the chair, takes a deep breath and lets it out, indicating the onset of relaxation and an experiential shift.]*

Clinician: As your out-breath gets fuller... easier... notice the tension automatically releasing from *those [another distancing term]* **uncomfortable areas throughout your body... with each out-breath... very good...**

[She eases in naturally and her breaths become more spaced and less effortful—a good signal for a patient with chronic pain. I find it's important not to spend too much time in the intensification, or deepening phase; just enough to ensure

she's absorbed and moving inwards. Often, teens struggling with chronic pain are sleep deprived; so, if there's too much intensification, they can slip into sleep. This could be therapeutic, but not at this stage when teaching her how to reduce her pain. However, once achieved, our next therapeutic goal would be using hypnosis for restorative sleep; e.g., addressing our "natural compulsion to sleep."]

On the next out-breath, travel into the center of your brain and nod your head when you are there... *[She nods.]* **Good... look around and see a set of switches...** *[Her eyes, under her eyelids, move horizontally, then she nods again.]* **Good! Now, these are not ordinary on-off switches. Notice... these switches are sophisticated dials, levers, or digital switches with markings from 10 down to 1. ... I'm not sure which kind yours are, but I know you'll know. ... When you've got them nod your head to let me know.**

[I wait until she nods, as this is teamwork. She needs to experience me respecting her pacing... she nods.]

Good, thanks! Now, look for the switch to the part of your body you wish to lower... and when you see what number it is, nod your head to let me know.

[Using the word "when" implies this is will happen, so it's just a matter of time before she finds it. In contrast, the term "if" invites the potential that this may not happen.]

Patient: *[Nods her head.]*

Clinician: Now that you've got it, you'll find it very easy to tell me, without disturbing your focus or experience, what number this switch is on, right now.

Patient: *[Takes a few moments, giving the impression of a process underway. Then in a soft voice says,]* **Seven.**

Clinician: Seven, okay. Now, see how this switch is connected up to the pain system, the brain circuitry and descending nerves down through the neck, down the spine to where *the* pain *has been* bothering you.

Patient: *[Takes a few moments, then nods.]*

> *[Therapeutically, I wish to create a different experience for her in relation to her pain. "The" in this placement is another distancing word to reduce her protectiveness or emotional attachment to the pain; "has been" places the experience in the past, freeing her to engage in the present in a new way with her physical experience.]*

Clinician: This can be so interesting, notice what's happening... some people see a color or intensity along those nerves which start to change... if you do, let me know.

Patient: *[Says nothing, but quietly nods.]*

> *[I note this and don't press her further, as I sense she's fully engaged with her introspective experience.]*

Clinician: Good... *[Affirming her process, the details of which I may or may not hear about later in our debrief.]*

Clinician: Now that you've got this... take in a deep energizing breath.

> *[Energy is often depleted in the experience of living in chronic pain—and to change the pain signal, directed energy is required. I mirror with more energy in my voice and a slightly quicker pace.]*

As you breathe in, hold your breath for a moment at the top—that's it!

Now, *[accruing energy for the shift ahead]* **grab your switch and as you breathe out... turn it down... down, so that the signal**

gets weaker and weaker... dimmer and dimmer... and color or intensity changes... so that you begin to notice changes, dimming in the bothersome sensation. That's it!

[Altering pain that has persisted for two years is a gradual process. I've found it more productive to suggest small shifts in awareness, in small steps, by using more tentative language such as "you begin to notice." If she runs on ahead of me and changes more rapidly that's great. But I'm not going to push her.]

Clinician: Good... now again! Deep energy breath in... hold it, grab your switch and turn it D... O... W... N... and notice the shifts in the sensation... and again... in your own time... you know what to do... noticing the changes, seeing, and feeling shifts in sensation, easing, dimming... comfort growing in ways that I don't even know right now... but you do... as you're now in the process of becoming boss of your own body... very good.... [Pause.] If there's anything you wish to tell me, you'll find it very easy to do so, while remaining fully in this experience.

[We're navigating into new territory, the experience of directly affecting one's own sensation. Note that I use the present participle, becoming, implying this an ongoing process... it continues.

I then pass the re-patterning process on to her so that she can do it in her own pace, and with my support she can develop more confidence in her own capacities. I notice her pacing. She is breathing more deeply and there is an intensity with which she is working. This informs me that she's fully engaged, and I know that there will be some change. We continue turning the switch further and further down with each deep exhale until I noticed a shift, an easing *in the intensity of her breath and posture. It seems she's reached a plateau, not uncommon in this process.]*

Clinician: In a moment... take a moment and travel back to your Pain Switch and let me know, what number it is on now?

Patient: Four.

[It is important to have realistic expectations when addressing pain that has persisted over time. First, any little change is progress. Second, expecting the pain to drop to zero is setting everyone up for disappointment. Remember, we're building a new, more productive relationship with pain, by providing the first therapeutic, integrated, physical-psychological-emotional experience. The Pain Switch allows a neutral engagement with previously feared pain and provides the frame for this experience, so that she can regard her pain more neutrally, then color, and rate it without emotional distress. From here we can build awareness that "You are not that pain! You are much more than that pain, and you can become boss of your own body!"]

Clinician: A four—that's excellent. Is that far enough for today? Or, would you like to continue...

[I now hand over the decision to empower her further. This is her body. She's in charge.]

Patient: A little more.

Clinician: Good... so now that you know how you access your Pain Switch, go ahead... breathe out... allow a deep energy breath in... that's it... and in your own time... grab your switch—you know exactly what to do!

[She continues a few more rounds, and when I see a stilling in her process, I pick it up.]

Clinician: Notice what has started to change... and where there is some easing. ... I'm curious to know, so take your time, check it out and when you've got it, you'll find it very easy to tell me your experience.

Patient: It's like a warm kind of softening in my back and down to my legs. ... The pain is there, but not sharp as before... it's better... but not gone...

Clinician: These are some good body changes, warming, softening that you were able to achieve by turning your pain switch down. ... You now have better control in your body... and the more you use it the better and stronger it responds. Where you are now?

Patient: Around a three-and-half or four.

[Patients with pain for some time will rarely be able to reduce their pain down or near to zero. Our goal is to create more flexibility in the brain-pain system, to not avoid but instead to learn to experience reducing sensation. Therefore, any change, even 0.005 out of 10, is affirmed.]

Clinician: Good you've done good work today! Before your re-orient, you have a choice whether or not you'd like to add on a "Pain Lock."

Optional Step: The Pain Lock

Patients sometimes become concerned that as soon as they re-orient back that the Pain Switch won't continue holding. If this is the case, the Pain Lock is an ideal addition. Sometimes, when re-orienting there can be shift, and pain can creep back as the person moves through the day. To address this, I developed the Pain Lock to support the transition into the rest of the day. Other times, as pain reductions become established, or to strengthen the patient's experience, the Pain Switch can be locked in place towards the end of the process. The entire process supports developing a greater respect for heeding pain signals and responding constructively without helplessness; for example, "Oooh, some pain... guess it's time to use my Pain Switch again!"

Clinician: If you wish, you can access your pain switch lock right now... to lock the changes in place... so that when you return to your day you know the lock supports the change you've attained. Do you wish to do that?

Patient: *[Nods yes.]*

Clinician: I'm not sure exactly how your lock looks, whether it's a combination lock, a lever, or it bolts the switch in place... but I do know that you know what's right for you right now.... Let me know with a nod when you've got it. ... *[She nods.]* **Good! Take a deep breath in, hold it as you grab your lock, locking it in place, so that it holds, and you sense the benefit of this added support... knowing you'll be able to move about your day with greater ease, comfort, and confidence.**

[I reiterate the frame of her process, empowering her to use this for herself, utilizing post-hypnotic suggestion to prime her for success.]

Clinician: You've done well! Now you know you can travel into your own pain system and activate and experience dimming your Pain Switch. It gets easier with each practice. ... The more you use it the easier it becomes.

[Post-hypnotic suggestion.]

Your brain-pain network learns, adapts, and changes to provide relief. Over time this becomes your new normal. The more you use it the stronger your relief-pattern becomes and the quicker you notice comfort growing...

[Stoking hope with more post-hypnotic suggestions.]

You are creating new, healthier patterns for yourself, having more control and confidence that you can have an easier life with a healthier connection with your body.

Take a moment to review what you experienced, achieved, and discovered... knowing that this is your first step and that many more will follow. In a moment, you'll find yourself re-orienting to this room. Feel the chair supporting you so that when you are ready, your eyes will open, as if they have a mind of their own... take your time...

[I remain quiet and provide the time and space for her re-alert.]

Patient: *[Her eyes open.]*

[Although her eyes open, she's still in a highly receptive, suggestive state. I remain respectful of this... then ask an open-ended question.]

Clinician: How was that?

[In this important de-brief process of 5 to 10 minutes, what she shares will guide my future work with her. It's important not to pepper her with questions, but to allow her sufficient time and space to share whatever she wishes.]

Patient: At first, I found it hard to see the Pain Switch, but as soon as I found the control room then all the switches were there and there was a big one flashing for my back and I knew that that was the one...

[Note the automaticity of the hypnotic response, the involuntary generating "all the switches were there" without any sense of intentional effort.

The final step is to set her up for regular home practice. Since I always make an audio recording of the hypnosis sessions, I send the recording to her iPhone. Teens with persistent pain need every bit of support. Knowing our session is close-by on her phone removes one more barrier to establishing new habits of creating pain-relief.]

Conclusion

The Pain Switch is one of many different hypnotic analgesic techniques. Designed to reduce pain intensity, it is direct and simple, drawing on the neurobiology of pain-brain processes. It requires considerable "set-up" in which naturalistic hypnotic suggestions foster engagement with teens who often are initially "resistant" to the consultation. There are other hypnotic techniques that address pain location, magnitude, and emotional or historic contributors to the current chronic pain condition. However, the Pain Switch has the advantage of being neutral and non-threatening as a first step to gauge how a patient responds to hypnosis for chronic pain—thus serving as a sound foundation for future individualized therapeutic hypnotic work.

References

Barber, J., & Adrian, C. (Eds.) (1982). *Psychological approaches to the management of pain*. New York, NY: Brunner/Mazel.

Jensen, M. P. (2009). Hypnosis for chronic pain management: A new hope. *Pain, 146,* 235-237.

Kohen, D. P., & Olness, K. (2011). *Hypnosis and hypnotherapy with children* (4th ed). New York, NY: Routledge.

Melzack, R., & Wall, PD. (1965). Pain mechanisms: a new theory. *Science, 150,* 971-979.

Melzack, R. (1999). From the gate to the neuromatrix. *Pain, Suppl 6,* S121-126.

Wood, C., & Bioy, A. (2008). Hypnosis and pain in children. *Journal of Pain and Symptom Management, 35,* 437-446.

Woolf, C. J. (2011). Central sensitization: Implications for the diagnosis and treatment of pain. *Pain, 152,* S2–15.

For Further Reading or Viewing

Kuttner, L. (2010). *A child in pain: What health professionals can do to help.* Bath, United Kingdom: Crown House.

Kuttner, L. (2013). *Dancing with Pain.* (20 mins). Documentary exploring chronic pain management for teens through the lens of dance. BC Children's Hospital Bookstore, Vancouver. http://bookstore.cw.bc.ca.

Yapko, M.D. (2018). *Taking hypnosis to the next level: Valuable tips for enhancing your clinical practice.* Fallbrook, CA: Yapko Publications.

CHAPTER 14

So, What am I Supposed to *Do* about these Headaches that keep Coming?

Daniel P. Kohen

"Dr. Dan," Minneapolis, Minnesota, is a former Professor of Pediatrics and Family Medicine and Community Health, and Director of Developmental-Behavioral Pediatrics Fellowship Training at the University of Minnesota. Following 35 years in academia, he maintains a private practice in Minneapolis. Dr. Kohen is sought after as a key speaker/faculty, author, and clinician. He has held leadership roles in the American Society of Clinical Hypnosis (ASCH), the Minnesota Society of Clinical Hypnosis (MSCH), and the American Board of Medical Hypnosis.

For 30 years he was the MSCH Director of Education and Training. He is a Fellow in the ASCH, the American Academy of Pediatrics, and the Society for Clinical and Experimental Hypnosis (SCEH). Dr. Kohen has taught all around the US and Canada and in 12 countries around the world for over 40 years. With Dr. Pam Kaiser, he spearheaded the emergence and evolution of the premier training organization for pediatric clinical hypnosis, the National Pediatric Hypnosis Training Institute (NPHTI) (www.nphti.org), a 501(c)(3) nonprofit organization.

Dr. Dan coauthored (with Dr. Karen Olness) the definitive text on pediatric hypnosis, Hypnosis and Hypnotherapy with Children, *4th ed. (2011), which has been translated into and published in French and German. He has authored over 90 published articles, book chapters, and abstracts. Dr. Kohen and Dr. Kaiser recently published an important summary article on the use of clinical hypnosis with children, entitled* "Clinical Hypnosis with Children and Adolescents—What? Why? How?: Origins, Applications, and Efficacy" *(Kohen & Kaiser, 2014).*

* * *

It is clear (to me) that the essential ingredients for any clinical encounter to be effective include the development of rapport, the careful development of the patient's (and parent's) history of the presenting problem/concern, and the noticing of the patient's responses (verbal and nonverbal) to continuing dialogue with the clinician. Rapport, history, and noticing, are, to be sure, ongoing, and inform each other as the therapeutic relationship and alliance unfolds, emerges, and develops over time (Kohen & Kaiser, 2014).

From the beginning, hypnotic elements can and should be integral to the process of rapport. Specific examples are evident as they are presented in the transcript which follows. Most notably, elements of Ericksonian suggestions and questions are embedded throughout; these may include: (1) considerable "wondering" about meaning and future orientation about "how will life be different *when* the problem is less or resolved?" (e.g., "What things one will be able to *do* differently *when* the problem is resolved?"); (2) re-framing of negative expectations and past negative experiences, pain, distress, and "bad" outcomes of the problem (of headaches) into potential positive outcomes following improvement and during progress toward resolution; and (3) the utilization of "HOW?" questions as described by Michael Yapko in *The Discriminating Therapist* (Yapko, 2016).

Such a participatory approach honors the reality that the patient is always the one that knows the most about his or her own problem. Therefore, s/he can and will benefit the most from an approach which engages perceptions, ideas, attitudes, and imaginative notions not only about what the desired outcome of help/therapy will/should be but also what the possibilities are for "*HOW* we are we going to get there?" By the Ericksonian principle of implication, this approach nurtures the idea that the therapist believes that the patient has internal resources available (perhaps yet to be discovered and defined) that can and will be put to work toward resolution of the problem. The seemingly simple shift of pronouns from "How are *you* going to get (to the resolution?)" to the plural, collaborative "we" conveys definitively the "I'll help you help yourself" concept that is foundational to the rapport essential in this Ericksonian, collaborative therapeutic approach (Erickson, 1958).

A methodical emphasis on precise use of various words is designed to enable the young person to begin to think differently about the problem. This sets the stage for change to be effected through specific hypnotic strategies and suggestions for implementation and integration of rehearsal of self-hypnosis, particularly of suggestions for amelioration, modulation, and elimination of headaches. Thus, very early (even the first few minutes of an initial visit), I commonly, gently but definitively interrupt at the mention of certain "negative" words. Using the words "excuse me," in combination with humor to deflect the potential negativity of an interruption, I point out that certain words are simply "not allowed" in my office. This situation often arises when a patient or parent says something like, "I've/we've tried everything and nothing helps." Sometimes, using a hand signal for "time-out," I may say, "Nothing has helped *yet....*" Although they have been interrupted, the vast majority of people do not quarrel with this and instead respond with "Right, nothing has helped *yet,*" already accepting this "re-framing." However, they often continue with their negative focus of "*but,* nothing we have *tried* works..." Using the "time-out" signal again, I often say, "I have to tell you that the words *try* and *tried* are not allowed in my office. I believe in *doing*, not *trying*." And I explain, "*try*" in our culture often—though not always—implies *failure*... and I'm focused on *success* (another re-frame).

Before the patient/family can protest or argue, I offer two quick, culturally current and positive "proofs" of my focus on *do*. First, I invite the patient to look again at the sign on the outside of my office door, which they likely missed and/or ignored when they first came in 20-30 minutes earlier. When they do look at the sign, they see a picture of "YODA" the "Jedi Master" and one of the heroes of the *Star Wars* films. His picture is accompanied by the well-known quote from the film *Episode V – The Empire Strikes Back,* in which Yoda, counseling and teaching Luke Skywalker about using "the Force", tells Luke Skywalker, "Do or do not, there is no try." Most children and families have some familiarity with this quote and respond with a smile and affirmation. The second "proof" is that the slogan for the athletic shoe manufacturer, Nike brand, is "Just Do it!" and not "Just Try it." Having firmly planted these seeds of expectation for positive outcomes and success, I usually just move on. It is notable that it is an implicit, and usually never mentioned again expectation, that they will not use the word "try" again. Often, if they even start to use the word "try," they self-correct before I can say anything.

Another example of word changes/re-framing specific to headache (or other pain problems) might be my response to "It really *hurts!*" or "It's really *terrible!*" In what I intend to be experienced paradoxically, and to create *confusion*, thus shifting focus, I might acknowledge, empathize, and at the same time introduce a re-framing by saying, "I know, I can tell it really *bothers* you, doesn't it?" This kind of re-frame to a different way of characterizing the discomfort while acknowledging, joining, and empathizing introduces and amplifies an invitation for the patient to alter their perception from, for example, "really terrible" to "really bother," or from "hurt" to "discomfort."

Other examples of specific word changes are reflected in the transcript presented later in this chapter. Sometime later in the same visit, and at an opportune pause and "teachable moment," I usually offer a very explicit explanation of this word-changing/re-framing approach. This might be something such as, "I'm sure you have noticed that not only have I interrupted you a few times but also that I have suggested changing a few words here and there." They agree that they have noticed this. I continue with, "I hope I haven't been rude, but it's *really important* and *here's why*: (Sometimes I actually print the following for them on a piece of paper or type it on the computer and print it out for them) *How* we *talk* is how we *think*. *How* we *think* is how we *feel* inside. *How* we *feel* is how we *act/behave*."

Continuing, I often add: "So, if we have some action or behavior we don't like (for example, headaches, worry, or habits) it may seem fine to say or think 'Just stop it!'—but that really doesn't work, does it? Ever been worried about something? (Everyone has!) Did someone who loves you/cares about you ever say 'Oh, don't worry...'?" Families always respond with *"Yes."* I ask, *"Did* that help you not worry anymore?" Everyone agrees *"No!"*

I say, "Similarly, when you are upset because of how bad you feel (for example, with a headache) did anyone ever say 'It can't be *that* bad?' Most often the person with the discomfort thinks—and may even say—'Oh, yes it *is that bad!!'* *But, when* we change how we *talk* about something, like referring to it as *really bothering* instead of *really hurting,* we can *begin* to *change* how we *think* about it. And *when* we begin to change how we *think* about it, *then* we can begin to *change how* we *feel* about it. And, of course, when we *change* how *we feel* about it, *then* it doesn't have to *bother* us nearly as much as before." Commonly, patients and parents lean back, take a deep breath, and say "Ohhhhhhh, I get it... right!"

All of that commonly precedes anything formally called hypnosis, or any formal or informal "induction" per se. Of course, elements of conversational hypnosis, future projection, re-framing, and the invitation to change are integral components of stage-setting for somewhat more formal hypnosis training and learning. Sometimes at the end of an initial visit, and more often at the beginning of the second visit, I continue with, "So, are you ready to learn something cool about managing and getting rid of those headaches (using "those" rather than "your" headaches is a dissociative suggestion) that used to (past tense) bother (re-frame) you?"

The vast majority of children and teens have an immediate *"Yes"* response. In the unlikely circumstance that they are uncertain, this means that pieces of rapport and/or history taking are yet to be established, and returning to rapport development and history would be appropriate in this case.

Transcript

The following transcript depicts the integration of indirect suggestion and re-framing into an initial encounter with a 12-year-old boy presenting with frequent migraine headaches. As the encounter unfolds, a "conventional history" is interwoven with the application of the utilization principle (Erickson, 1958) to develop rapport, understand and re-frame the nature of the symptoms, identify patient strengths, resources, expectations, and motivation, and to plant the seeds of positive therapeutic suggestions; all to be integrated into a somewhat more formalized hypnotic experience before the conclusion of the encounter.

Clinician: So, I wonder why you came to see me today.

[This is purposely directed to the child to convey the expectation that the clinician is interested in the child's perception, his views, and his language (and not only those of his parents). This approach will positively drive the rapport and the positive therapeutic relationship that is integral to an expectation for a positive outcome. Use of this personal approach throughout the encounter is intended to promote and enhance the patient's comfort, self-confidence, and self-control.]

Patient: Well, I've been having these terrible migraines almost every day or every other day. The pain is excruciating, I can't DO anything, I'm missing school, and I love school...

Clinician: Wow... it sure sounds like they bother you a great deal and really get in your way...

[Re-framing of "terrible migraines" and "pain is excruciating" to "bother a lot" introduces at once a direct

acknowledgement of the discomfort and its impact while invitating alteration of perception from "excruciating pain" to "bother," indirectly conveying the idea that change is possible.]

Clinician: Can you help me understand your discomfort? Let's say we had a scale from 0 to 12, like a regular old 12-inch ruler. Can you tell me something about the headaches; like if 12 is "the worst imaginable headache in the world anyone could ever have" and 0, of course, is "no headache at all," then *[of course, ask only those of the following that are appropriate in the therapeutic context, although most will be]:*

- **What is the average level of your headache when it starts?**

- **What is the highest on average one goes?**

- **What is the highest *you* have ever had?**

- **How high does it have to be to make you cry?**

- **How high does it have to be to make you vomit?**

- **How high does it have to be to keep you from being your regular self?**

[All of these questions are designed to provide expectations that this chronic, recurrent pain is not as terrible as it often seems, that one headache is not the same as another, and that like most things in life, it is not black or white, but various shades of gray. The answers to these questions, i.e., acknowledgement that it can be, for example, an "11" or it can be "7," or "5," or "8" offer the unspoken suggestion that by definition it can become lower (go down), and even, perhaps be "1" or "zero"; with the only remaining question becoming HOW how to lower it (Yapko, 2016). So, all of

these questions are tone-setting and are intentional, expectation-creating suggestions at one level, while at the conscious level they are "ordinary and legitimate" history-taking questions.]

Clinician: Thanks, so let's continue. I wonder…

- **How *low* does it have to be for you to *be able to do most or all of your regular activities*, like ride your bike, or watch TV?**

- **How *low* does it have to be for you to *be able to fall asleep*?**

- **How *low* does it have to be for you to *be able to go to school*?**

["Wondering" communicates to the pre-teen patient a message of some uncertainty that the clinician "needs help" understanding. This "recruiting" of contemplation drives the rapport and the growing potential for a positive expectation for a positive outcome in the child. All of these questions are different by focusing upon the headaches getting lower, and therefore, better. The underlying nature of these questions as compliments makes them implicit compliments. Thus, in a sense, they are also ego-strengthening suggestions that say, without saying, that the clinician trusts that the patient knows these things about their headaches, even if they didn't know that they knew. By asking these questions in this way, the suggestion is embedded that if the headaches can be "9" or "10," they surely have been and can be "1" or "0."]

Clinician: Great… thanks. So, I guess *all* we really need to do then, is to find a way to easily and quickly get to "3" or "4" *[if that is the level at which they can be their "regular self"]* **on**

the way to getting to "1" or "0." I think you're going to be pleasantly surprised to find out how easy that can be.

[Saying, "ALL we really need to do" is another statement of implication; that is, it means "this is easier than I thought it was going to be....". Since they already said "3" or "4" is a level at which they can do most anything, it's a truism to indicate that it's not only easy but desirable and good to get to "3" or "4" on the way to "0." No one disagrees with what amounts to another positive future suggestion, albeit in the not yet officially hypnotic state.]

Clinician: I'm not sure yet how you'll do that [i.e., lower the level of the headache], but we'll find out. I'll also tell you how some other kids have gotten rid of their migraines that used to bother them.

[These are future-oriented, positive expectancy suggestions. They do not say "if" he will lower the headaches, but, rather, how; confidently implying both that it will happen and that "We'll find out." The suggestions also pave the way for storytelling about others who have been successful eliminating headaches. Note, saying, "...that used to bother" means, of course, that being bothered is in the past and is no longer problematic.]

Clinician: [Seeming to be changing the subject,] So, what do you do for fun?

[This apparent non sequitur has several purposes. One purpose is to continue to develop rapport by amplifying that the clinician is interested personally in who the boy is, what he likes to do, and how he has fun. The clinician is not only interested in or focused on the "migraine" but is also interested in the guy who has the migraine. It also serves the purpose of matter-of-factly learning about some of the kinds *of activities that may be useful content for imagery for the patient during the forthcoming hypnotic experience.]*

Patient: I play soccer, I write songs and play guitar, I hang out with my friends and play video games.

Clinician: *[After garnering some details about each of the favorite activities,]* **You said you're one of the best players on your soccer team. *HOW* did you get to be so good?**

Patient: Doing it over and over, you know, *practice*.

Clinician: And how about guitar and writing songs, how did you learn to do those?

Patient: Well, I took lessons for a while but then I just started hearing songs in my head and writing them; they just come into my mind.

Clinician: Wow, that's terrific. So, the more you do something, the better you get, and sometimes it seems to just happen and pops into your mind?

Patient: Yeah.

[This line of conversation serves a dual purpose. On their face, the questions and the dialogue that follows further reinforce rapport development, getting to know the patient and his or her perceptions of his or her signature strengths. At a perhaps less-than-conscious level, the questions can also be used to elicit and identify (some of) the patient's internal resources and can lay the foundation for their use as metaphorical suggestions, reinforcing development of competency. Well before any "official" or more formal use of hypnosis, these indirect, so-called "waking suggestions" are intended to reinforce the idea that when someone already understands that "the more you do something (i.e., practice)

the better you get," they can indeed then learn to apply this same resource, skill, and expectation to resolving and solving other problems, such as in this case, migraine headaches.]

Clinician: So, are you ready to learn something cool about how you can use your mind and skills you *already have*, in order for you to be more in charge of those headaches that used to bother you more?

[This trance-sitional suggestion does many things. It introduces a shift and checks in with the patient on their "readiness" to proceed to something new (now that a nice, beginning rapport is established). It also offers ego-strengthening compliments (about skills he "already has") and introduces the future-oriented hypnotic suggestion that he can be "in charge" of the headaches, while implying that they may already be changing because they "used to" bother more. It is exceedingly unusual for a young patient to say "No" or to hesitate in response to this question about proceeding, but if they do say "No" it likely means they are not ready and one should not proceed without discussing and understanding their hesitation.]

This is really easy and fun... you sit there, I'll sit here.

[Setting the tone for what happens next, and offering assurance that it is not only easy, but also fun. The "you sit there, I'll sit here" comment is an indirect assurance of safety, even if there has been no comment about, or reason to expect, that safety is a concern.]

I'm just going to talk about imagination and daydreaming, and muscles relaxing, and breathing easily—all stuff you already know—and all you have to do is listen, there's no work to do.

[This "pre-(formal) hypnosis" preparation is intended to be reassuring. "Just" means something is easy; this is reinforced by "stuff you already know." "All you have to do" reinforces easiness.]

Go ahead and close your eyes, or keep them open until they close by themselves... either way is fine. With your eyes closed you don't have to be distracted by things around you here, and actually, having your eyes closed allows you to see things more clearly.

[This is where the word "insight" comes from, seeing things more clearly or "sight in-side" your mind. The presentation of choices or a "double bind" of eyes closed or open until they close themselves is a suggestion for comfort and control, giving the illusion of "choosing" eye closure and also suggesting dissociation; "they close by themselves." Providing the reason for doing a suggestion is often important. Hence, I say, "...eyes closed allows you to see things more clearly." Internally, patients understand this also as a suggestion for <u>better understanding</u>, as they know that's what "seeing things clearly" also means.]

Just *[i.e., it's easy!]* imagine or daydream that you're not even here. I don't know where you'll be, but *you* will know because it's *your* imagination. Maybe you'll imagine that you are playing soccer, or maybe you're hanging out with friends playing video games, or watching YouTube, or maybe you're at home in your room or some other favorite room in the house playing guitar and creating some new ideas for a song... or maybe something else like a vacation. Wherever it is, just be there as though you were really there because you really ARE there in your imagination...

[Focusing on imagined experiences familiar to the patient typically is reinforcing of comfort and a sense of control. Offering choices within clearly defined boundaries provides continued enhancement that this is the patient's experience and the clinician is the coach, teacher, facilitator.]

While you're there *[or, "imagining being there"]* notice everything about it; the weather there, the sounds there, the smells and tastes that are part of this imagination. Notice who's there with you, how things are going. If it's a soccer game, then what the score is and how well you're playing; if it's a video game, then how well you're doing and how much you're enjoying it. Maybe you're with family, or friends, or maybe you're alone like when you play guitar and write songs. … I don't know, but *you'll know* because it's *your* imagination and *you* are the boss of it and *you can make it* as *wonderful* as you want and need. It's great to know that the more you do it, the better you get—just like soccer or music or learning to be the *boss* of those headaches.

[Multisensory imagery is intended to intensify (deepen) and expand the experience of the trance. Details are offered to enhance personal control, and further introduction is offered that this experience can be used to learn how to be the boss of the headaches.]

Probably, while you have been doing this you have noticed a couple of things that have happened, kind of all by themselves. I'll bet you noticed *[and if they hadn't, they will now!]* that your breathing has gotten slower and that's because when the mind is relaxed doing imagination, the body listens and breathing gets slower; and that's great! It also means that you are doing this exactly right.

[Everyone likes to know that they are doing something new the RIGHT way, so this ego-strengthening compliment is intentional early in this more structured part of the hypnotic experience.]

So, each time that you breathe *out* pay attention to how tension goes away and to a way that you do that...

["Word play" on attention to tension and to "the way-goes away" and "a way that you do that" are intended to reinforce focus, and by some confusion, to intensify the experience.]

and to the natural way...

[It's effortless and easy.]

that your body relaxes automatically with each... next... breath... out.

[Verbalization paced to exhalation. This introduction to progressive relaxation is intended to intensify and deepen the trance and to set the tone for specific hypnotic suggestions for headache management and prevention which follow.]

Every time that you breathe out, the next group of muscles can become loose, soft, comfortable, and relaxed... just the right amount for you each time you do this. When the relaxation passes your neck and moves into your shoulders, it doesn't matter whether the left shoulder gets relaxed first or the right, or both together. ... As soon as the relaxation gets all the way to the turn at the elbows and starts down into your forearms, let your head nod so that I'll know that's happening and you notice it...

[Then wait for the head to nod in ideomotoric fashion and acknowledge it with "Great!" or "Thanks!" This form of progressive relaxation should be paced both to what the

clinician observes happening and/or to what the patient verifies by the ideomotoric head nod. Note that "let the head nod" is a request for an unconscious, ideomotoric movement, whereas "Nod your head" may be okay, but is a request for a conscious movement. The request "let your head nod... so that I'll know" is an invitation for communication with the clinician. When it "happens" it is ratification that the trance is indeed happening, and it can be the beginning of perhaps using this form of communication in trance as the clinical encounter continues.

Following gradual progressive relaxation down the rest of the body and occasionally "checking in," for example, "let me know when relaxing gets all the way to the _____, good!"]

It's good to know that as you continue instructing/allowing all of the muscles to relax just the right amount that it gets easier and easier to do the more you do it, and it doesn't matter if you're a little bit behind or way ahead of what I'm saying because you're the boss of your mind, your body, and your relaxation. ... *Now,* **when your relaxing gets all the way to your ankles, feet, and toes, take a deep breath and as you let it out notice how good it feels to let any remaining tension just flow out through the bottom of your feet into the ground. ... Let me know when that has happened.**

[Wait for the ideomotor signal. This intensification is intended to deepen (intensify) the trance, to teach self-control and the creation of comfort while setting the stage for then using the trance to work on and solve the presenting problem, in this case, migraine headaches. Waiting for the ideomotor signal is, of course, an example of pacing before again leading.]

When your body is as relaxed as you need it to be for now, and you are continuing to enjoy your imagination *and* you are ready to learn how to use these good feelings and state of mind to be the *boss* of those headaches, let me know *[and wait for the ideomotor signal].*

> *[This is intended to check in with the patient, and to affirm his or her readiness to move on to the next phase of how to use the trance for his or her benefit.]*

Thanks. You are doing this really well! While you continue to enjoy wherever you are in your imagination, in another part of your mind—over *there somewhere*—just notice that scale or ruler that you were using in your mind to measure those headaches. ... You know, it goes from "zero" (no headaches) to "12" (the worst imaginable headache). Let me know when you see it there in your mind somewhere.

> *["Over there somewhere" reinforces that he will see the scale somewhere in his mind, that it's his and that he can use it. "Let me know" is a request, building on the earlier suggestions to respond with an ideomotoric head nod or, of course, some other signal of his choosing.]*

Of course, it doesn't matter where exactly it is as long as you see it. I don't know if it's in the sky, or along the neck of your guitar, or on the soccer scoreboard, or if it's a wooden ruler on the kitchen table... but you'll know because it's *yours*. Notice what it's made out of—wood or metal or plastic, and what color it is. Or maybe it's white and is in the clouds?

Then, notice what number *it* is on right now there in your imagination. Maybe you'll know by an arrow pointing to it or by the number lighting up or being a different color. ...

When you notice, let me know, either by showing me the number with your fingers, or by saying it. No hurry.

> [*This reinforces choices of how to picture the scale but also that he will notice the scale because he is motivated to make a change and he wants to find out how to do that. The patient will indicate a number by speaking it or by holding up the equivalent number of fingers. IF the response is "zero" then...*]

Wonderful, now just store that "zero" in your mind so that in the *future* you can always *get* a "zero" when you need it. *Now* have a pretend headache, not a real one—that would be silly/ridiculous—and notice what number the *[pretend or not]* headache is on. ... Maybe it's a "3" or "4," or a "6" or "7," or an "8" or 9?" Let me know the number... *[Patients states the number]* thanks. Would it be okay with your inside mind if that (number) goes *down*?

> [*The implication, of course, is that it can go down and both subject and clinician know that this is the agreed-upon goal. It's incredibly rare for the patient to say it's not okay for it to go down.*]

I'm not sure *how* you *will* lower it and feel better. Kids do this in different ways. I'll tell you how some of my patients have done it before to help their problem get way better and then to go away. This one kid I knew was an 11-year-old girl.

> [*The first story I tell is always about a child of the opposite sex who is a year younger than the current patient. This is to reinforce the patient's inescapable internal thought that, "Well, if an 11-year-old girl (or boy if the patient is a girl) can do this, then I sure can..." but without any necessity of saying that.*]

And, what she told me that she *did* was every time she had a headache she imagined she was on an elevator, like at a huge department store or hotel; and she was on whatever floor the headache was on and the numbers of the floors in the elevator were her "ruler." So, if she was on "8," she said she'd just [*i.e.,* "*It's easy*"] picture in her mind that she pushed the button for "7" and the light would go off at "8" and on at "7"... then "6" and the light would... go off at "7"... and on at "6"... and then "3"... and in a few moments the "3" would light up... and then it would go zooming all the way down to "zero"; and the door would open and she would walk out with a big smile and no more headache.

I once told that story to a 9-year-old boy who said he was afraid of elevators so before he learned how to get rid of elevator fear, he put *his* ruler on a water slide, where "12" was at the top of the slide and "zero" was at the bottom, and wherever his headache was he'd just slide *down* the slide in his imagination 11-10-9-8-7-6-5-4-3-2-1-0 and splash around happy in the COOL refreshing swimming pool water...

Then there was this 5-year-old girl who pretended that she could go for a trip around her own body... she pretended she was so tiny she could go inside her body under a fingernail, or through her belly button, or down through her nose... and she'd get onto a jet ski or into a speedboat in her blood and travel all around her body and pretty soon she'd go right up the neck to that main computer center we call the brain and she'd park the jet ski outside and go into the main computer center. And there inside her brain she'd see all the different switches and dials and computer screens with number scales; and she found the one that said "M" for migraine or "H" for headaches and she turned it *d o w w w w w n n n*... just like turning the volume down on a CD player or TV or smartphone... from "7" to "6," "6" to "5," "5" to "4," "4" to "3," "3" to "2," "2" to "1" and "1" to "zero". And she locked it on "zero" and was so happy and proud that she could do that. Each of these kids told me I could tell their story to others as long as I didn't say their name, 'cause that's private. Each of them got totally rid of their headaches... some took a few weeks and got gradually better... others took a little longer. None stayed the same and of course none got worse... why would they?!

I'm not sure which way *you* will lower *your* ruler to improve your migraine before it goes away completely, but you'll discover that in your mind. Maybe it will be like one of the stories, or maybe it'll have something to do with soccer, or the scale will be like playing a scale on your guitar, or something else. Maybe when we're done today you'll tell me *how* you *did* it, or maybe you'll want to keep it private for a while... that's all up to you of course.

> [Stories are metaphors for the possibility of change that are geared to the developmental level of understanding of the individual child or teen, while amplifying choice. Thus, the use of the word "pretend" instead of "imagination" for the 5-year-old's story. Returning reference to "I don't know but you'll know" is designed to repeatedly reinforce that the trance and manner of healing/change is an internal decision of the patient, and is intended to continue to empower and reinforce the emerging positive belief in self-efficacy and self-confidence. Reference to "keeping it private" is to provide the option for discussion post-hypnosis, particularly if like some children, the patient does not have specific or sufficient cognitive recall or either the willingness or ability in the moment to articulate the nature of their just-completed experience. If that is the case, then the option of keeping it

private can be comfortably invoked without worry or feeling bad for not sharing the nature of their imagery (Kohen & Kaiser, 2014; Kohen & Olness, 2011).]

Once you have lowered the headache as much as you want and need for today you can store up the "zero" or another very low number in a file in your computer we call the brain. That way, any time in the future if you do get another migraine, you can not only get relief and comfort as you have done so well today, but you could also just open the file with the "zero", get a "zero" there to feel better right away and just drag the headache number to the trash and delete it. It is possible, you know, that you have already had your whole life's quota of migraines and you won't have any more anyway.

[This is setting the tone for beginning to conclude the experience, as well as offering post-hypnotic suggestions for how to do this in the future.]

In a few moments, *when* you are comfortable that you have learned something really cool and you know how to do it for yourself really well, *then* you can begin to complete your imagination for today and be back completely here. *Before* you do that, give yourself an inside-your-mind message that you know exactly what to do *when* you practice this at home 2 or 3 times each day for 5 or 10 minutes. When you practice even when you don't have a headache that makes it *much easier* to do it right away *when* a headache comes, *if* you ever get another one.

I don't know if your practices will be before or after breakfast, after school, before supper, or even before going to sleep at night. *Remind* yourself that you learned really well *how* to begin with closing your eyes, imagine being somewhere you enjoy doing something you really like, *then* notice your breathing is slower, *then* let your body relax from head to toe as you breathe out slowly (or maybe it will be from toes up to head, either is okay), and after you are as relaxed as you need to be, *then* picture your scale in your mind and watch however you decide to *lower it*, as much as you need to. It will be *easy to remember* to practice having a pretend headache even if you don't have one when you are practicing. *That* way your mind will know exactly what to if you do get one. *Then*, store up the low numbers or the zeroes, and come back to your regular feelings, and when you leave your imagination, *be sure to bring your good feelings and "zero"* with you when you come back here. Then when you've told yourself those things, you'll be finished, and when you're finished you'll be done.

> [*Clinician remains silent as patient alerts. The use of when-then is repeated as before for amplification of the truism that change will happen. Suggestions are offered to set the tone that completion is soon to happen (preparing for alerting by "before you end..."); and before that, post-hypnotic suggestions are offered for the importance of daily self-hypnosis practice, and for review of the sequential steps of self-hypnosis that took place during this session. Termination of trance—without any "counting"—is from "when you're finished you'll be done" and by the indirect suggestion of changing focus by the clinician becoming silent after having been talking prior to that. Being sure to have left 5 to 7 minutes or longer for de-briefing after the completion of the hypnosis.*]

Are you all the way back here now? So, what did you *notice*?

[Presumption by clinician that the patient indeed noticed (hopefully) many things and offers the invitation to discuss what was noticed. It is essential to take the time to have this important open-ended conversation and to realize that in this post-hypnosis time the patient is still highly suggestible; it is an opportunity for waking-suggestion reinforcement, thus:]

I wonder what you will *do when* you practice? What two times each day do you think you'll choose to practice being more in charge of those *[not "your"]* headaches?

[Even if the patient doesn't want to or can't seem to easily articulate what went on in the just-completed hypnotic experience, this comment offers the clear expectation for doing the homework of practicing several times a day. It also invites the patient to say something about what they think they'll do when they practice. This example of the contents of the first session is, of course, just the beginning. All of the skills will be reinforced in future visits.]

References

Kohen, D.P., & Kaiser, P. (2014). Clinical hypnosis with children and adolescents—What? Why? How?: Origins, applications, and efficacy. *Children, 1*, 74-98.

Erickson, M.H. (1958). Naturalistic techniques of hypnosis. *American Journal of Clinical Hypnosis, 2*, 3-21.

Yapko, M. D. (2016). *The discriminating therapist.* Fallbrook, CA: Yapko Publications.

Kohen, D. P., & Olness, K. (2011) *Hypnosis and hypnotherapy with children* (4th ed). New York, NY: Routledge.

For Further Reading

Jensen, M. P. (2009). Hypnosis for chronic pain management: A new hope. *Pain, 146*, 235-237.

Jensen, M. P. (2011). *Hypnosis for chronic pain management: Therapist guide*. New York, NY: Oxford University Press.

Kohen, D.P. (2017). Headaches. In Elkins, G. (Ed), *Handbook of medical and psychological hypnosis: Foundations, applications, and professional issues* (pp. 259-271). New York, NY: Springer Publishing.

Kohen, D.P., & Zajac, R. (2007). Self-hypnosis training for headaches in children and adolescents. *Journal of Pediatrics, 150*, 635-639.

Kohen, D.P. (2010). Long-term follow-up of self-hypnosis training for recurrent headaches: What the children say. *International Journal of Clinical and Experimental Hypnosis, 58*, 417-432.

Kohen, D.P. (2011). Chronic daily headache: Helping adolescents help themselves with self-hypnosis. *American Journal of Clinical Hypnosis, 54*, 32-46.

ABOUT THE EDITOR

Mark P. Jensen, PhD, is a Professor and Vice Chair for Research at the Department of Rehabilitation Medicine, University of Washington, in Seattle, Washington, USA. He has been studying chronic pain and helping individuals effectively manage pain for over 30 years. He has been funded by the National Institutes of Health and other funding agencies to study the efficacy and mechanisms of different treatments for chronic pain, including hypnosis. He has published extensively (seven books and over 500 articles and book chapters) on the topics of pain assessment and treatment.

He has has received numerous awards for his writing and scientific contributions including: the Jay Haley Early Career Award for Innovative Contributions to Hypnosis from the International Society of Hypnosis, the Clark L. Hull Award for Scientific Excellence in Writing on Experimental Hypnosis from the *American Journal of Clinical Hypnosis*, the Wilbert E. Fordyce Clinical Investigator Award from the American Pain Society, and both the Distinguished Contributions to Scientific Hypnosis and Distinguished Contributions Professional Hypnosis Awards from the American Psychological Association Division 30, among others.

His book on the use of hypnosis for chronic pain management (*Hypnosis for Chronic Pain Management: Therapist Guide*, published by Oxford University Press) won the 2011 Society for Clinical and Experimental Hypnosis Arthur Shapiro Award: Best Book on Hypnosis. He is the President-Elect of the International Society of Hypnosis, and a popular international speaker and workshop facilitator.

CPSIA information can be obtained
at www.ICGtesting.com
Printed in the USA
FFHW010918050519
52214452-57596FF

9 781946 832085